Draper L. Kauffman, Jr.

Systems One: An Introduction to Systems Thinking

The Innovative Learning Series

Systems One: An Introduction to Systems Thinking
© 1980 by Future Systems, Inc.

This text originally entitled *The Human Environment: An Introduction to Enviromental Systems* was developed under a grant from the Office of Environmental Education, Office of Education, Department of Health, Education, and Welfare.

ISBN 978-0-9647-0442-8

Illustration: Frederick Stout

Publishing Consultant: Joanne Simons

Contents

Foreword ii

Chapter 1:   What Is a System 1

Chapter 2:   Stability 6

Chapter 3:   Things in Common 13

Chapter 4:   Change and Growth 20

Chapter 5:   Putting the Pieces Together 25

Chapter 6:   Complex Systems 29

Appendix: System Notes 38

The purpose of the Innovation Learning Series is to satisfy the need for educational material required to provide people with mental tools with which to cope with the increasing complexity of modern life. The objective of the series is to bridge the gap between what the *Learning Report* of the Club of Rome has termed "maintenance learning" and "innovative learning." The Report, entitled *No Limits to Learning*, stresses the need to evaluate long-term consequences of one's decisions, to consider the second order consequences or side effects of one's actions, to detect signs of future problems, to think about the whole as well as the parts, to see multiple rather than single causes and effects, and to detect interrelationships and to recognize their importance.

Foreword

It's no secret that the world we live in is a complicated one, and that it is growing more complicated all the time. Problems like pollution, energy shortages, inflation, unemployment, crime, and urban decay affect all of us, yet it is difficult for us to know how to deal with them.

No one can be an expert on every subject. But when we turn to the experts for help, they often seem confused and isolated from the real issues, arguing with each other and looking at only those pieces of a problem that happen to fit into their own particular specialties. Indeed, it often seems that the more people learn about the world we live in, the harder it becomes to get a real understanding of how the whole world works.

So what are we to do? Just mind our own business and ignore everything else? Unfortunately, "everything else" has a habit of invading our personal lives in a most unpleasant way if we ignore it. For example, suppose that you decide on a career that appeals to you. You spend years training for it, gaining experience, and working your way up. It's a good job and you're good at it. Then suddenly the job is wiped out, eliminated by economic changes, new technology, environmental pollution, or because of a change in political priorities. These forces may be beyond your control, but if you understand how they work you can at least *anticipate* them and prepare to cope with them.

The same is true of all sorts of private, personal decisions. The wisdom of one choice or another depends on what is happening in the rest of our society. Furthermore we all have a stake in developing and maintaining a safe and humane environment. If we, as citizens, don't understand the big, complex problems affecting our environment, then the right decisions won't get made and we will all be worse off. (In fact, as we will see, leaving these problems to politicians and "experts" almost guarantees that we will get solutions which don't work and which often make the problems worse.)

In other words, we all need to understand the world around us, just to survive, but we can't possibly become experts in every subject. Is there any way out of this trap? Surprisingly, there *is* a way—and a fairly easy way—to learn how to deal with the world around us in all its complexity without being some kind of mental superman. The answer is an approach we can call "systems thinking," and the purpose of this book is to introduce you to it.

Expectations

Those are big claims. If "systems thinking" can do all that, why isn't it more widely known? In the first place, schools are usually slow to change the subjects they teach. This subject is still a new one and it seems quite strange to people who were trained in the traditional way. A second reason, and perhaps the most important one, is that most of what has been written about systems thinking has been extremely technical, full of mathematics, and difficult to read. Only recently has anyone made much of an attempt to translate the ideas of systems thinking for a non-expert.

And that, of course, is what this book is about. It doesn't require a background in math or science and the jargon has been kept to a minimum. It *will* require a moderate amount of effort from you, mostly in re-thinking things you already know. If you are willing to put that effort into it, here's what you can expect:

1. *Learning new subjects* will be easier. Most subjects are taught in complete isolation from each other. If you take a course in biology and then a course in U.S. government, no connection is made between the two and you have to start the government course from scratch. Actually, much of what you learned about biological systems applies to political systems (and vice versa); instead of having to start all over again, you can build on what you have already learned. The basic rules of how systems work apply to social systems, political systems, economic systems, ecological systems, and physical systems. Once you understand these rules you can tackle each new subject or problem by building on what you already know.

2. You will learn how to make *complex problems* and situations easier to understand. Most schools never deal with solving problems that cross the boundaries between different disciplines and most people never get a chance to learn how to make messy problems more manageable. Taking a systems approach to such problems doesn't guarantee right answers, but it does increase your chances.

3. You will get some suggestions about *effective strategies* for influencing the world around you. When people see things they want to change, they often spend their efforts in ineffective ways, and they get very frustrated as a result. A systems approach can help you identify "high leverage points" in the systems where your efforts will have a greater chance of success.

4. Finally, you will get some help in developing a *comprehensive world view* of your own. Both in school and out, most people are exposed to knowledge in bits and pieces and get very little help in tying these chunks together into an overall pattern that makes sense. Whether you can create such a pattern for yourself over the years is largely up to you, but a systems approach at least provides a consistent frame of reference and a way of fitting the pieces together as you come to them.

Chapter One:
WHAT IS A SYSTEM

For many centuries scientists believed that the best way to learn more about something they didn't understand was to take it apart and find out what it was made of. This approach had been quite successful, particularly in biology, chemistry, and physics. However, there is always the danger when anything is successful that people will want to take it too far. In this case, the extreme is called "reductionism"—the idea that something is *nothing but* the sum of its parts. This *sounds* reasonable, but it leads to the illogical conclusion that there is no difference between a comfortable house and a pile of building materials, or between a frisky mouse and a test tube full of chemicals.

The difference, of course, between the molecules in a mouse and those in a test tube full of chemicals is *organization*. The molecules in a mouse are organized in a precise and complex way, while those in the test tube are just sloshed together. Most scientists realized that it was important to understand how the pieces fit together, at least in their own field, but they were still mostly concerned about the "parts" rather than about the "pattern."

"... molecules in a mouse are organized ..."

One of the results of this attitude was the division of the sciences into many different specialties. Because the basic units of each subject are so different, it seemed that the ways these units were organized must *also* be unique, and that various specialties therefore had little in common with each other. The result was that the experts in each speciality developed their own specialized theories and their own specialized languages to describe them. Eventually, this meant that scientists in different fields could no longer understand each other and that the public couldn't understand any of them without years of study.

Then, beginning in the 1920's, a group of researchers began to make a serious study of the *patterns themselves,* the ways in which all different kinds of "systems" were organized. And they made a startling discovery; no matter how different the ingredients of different systems looked, they were all put together according to the *same* general rules of organization! For the first time, there was a way of linking together all of the scattered fields of knowledge and showing what they had in common.

This new field, which is known as "general systems theory," began to have a powerful impact almost immediately. It has revolutionized many fields of science and has had an enormous impact on all our lives, even though most people have never heard of it. Among other things, it made possible the development of sophisticated computers and automation, and its practical application as "systems analysis" is an essential tool for the management of all kinds of businesses and institutions.

Its two most important contributions are only now being realized, however. The first is that systems theory provides a way of tackling those big, messy, real-world problems which don't fit neatly into various specialities, just at a time when we face a whole batch of problems so serious that they threaten the survival of our society. The second is that general systems theory provides a way for average people to get a good, clear picture of how their environment works without spending their lives studying all the details of every subject.

The Idea of "System"

An understanding of how systems work has to begin, of course, with an idea of what a system is. Fortunately, we are going to use the word "system" in its everyday sense, as in "nervous system," or "legal system," or the "cooling system" in a car. In other words, *a system is a collection of parts which interact with each other to function as a whole.* The cooling system in a car, for example, may consist of a radiator, a fan, a water pump, a thermostat, a cooling jacket, and

"Dividing a cow in half does not give you two smaller cows."

several hoses and clamps. Together they function to keep the engine from overheating, but separately they are useless. To do the job, *all* of the parts must be present *and* they must be arranged in the proper way. Moving one end of a hose just an inch is enough to put the whole cooling system (and the car) out of commission.

If something is made up of a number of parts and it does *not* matter how those parts are arranged, then we are dealing with a "heap" and not a system. (A pile of sand, for example, remains essentially unchanged even if you stir it around and change the location of specific grains of sand.) Another difference between "systems" and "heaps" is that "heaps" are not essentially changed by adding to the size of the heap or taking some parts away from it. Adding more milk to the milk already in a pail just gives you a larger amount of milk, but adding another cow to the one you already have does *not* give you a larger cow. In the same way, pouring half the milk into a second pail gives you two smaller amounts of milk, but dividing the cow in half does *not* give you two smaller cows. You may end up with a lot of hamburger, but the essential nature of "cow"—a living system capable, among other things, of turning grass into milk—would be lost. This is what we mean when we say that a system functions as a "whole". Its behavior depends on its entire structure and not just on adding up the behavior of its different pieces.

This brings up a logical question: if the pieces of one system act together as a single unit, why can't that system be a "piece" of some other system? The answer is that it certainly *can* be part of a larger system. If it is, we call it a "subsystem" of the larger system. And that larger system, of course, can be a subsystem of a still larger system. In fact, this pattern of systems being part of larger systems which are part of still larger systems, and so on, is something we will find wherever we look, in all parts of the human environment.

For example, since we have been talking about cows, let's take a look at the chain of smaller and larger systems to which the cow belongs. A cow, like any living thing, is a very complex system in its own right, but it is also part of a number of larger systems. If it is kept with other cows, it will be part of a highly organized social system called a "herd". Each herd has a leader ("Bossie") and a chain of command as clearly defined and strictly enforced as in a military unit. If we are primarily interested in learning how a herd works, then we think of the herd as the basic system and each of the cows as a subsystem of the herd.

On the other hand, if we are primarily interested in learning how a cow "works," we would treat the cow as the basic system and try to learn something about its subsystems—such as its circulatory system, nervous system, reproductive system, and digestive system—and how they work together to enable the cow to stay alive and do the various things that cows do. In fact, we can continue this process of looking at smaller and smaller subsystems until we get clear down to the level of atomic particles.

The illustration on the next page shows how such a "ladder" or "hierarchy" of systems would look if we started with one particular atom in one cell of your own brain and worked our way up from there as many levels as we can go.

Each system on the list combines with other systems of about the same level to make up the next larger system. Thus a particular protein molecule might contain atoms of carbon, hydrogen, oxygen, and nitrogen; an economy is made up of people, land, buildings, machines, plants, dairy herds, and so on; the solar system is made up of the sun, the planets and their moons, and many, many asteroids, comets, and other bits of debris. If we had started at a different point—say, for example, an atom in a cow's brain—our list would have looked a little different in the middle, but it would still consist of a similar set of steps, with smaller systems combining to make larger systems which combine with others to make still larger systems.

Why is this true? If you stop to think about it, this neat progression of steps, from the smallest particle up to the entire universe, does seem rather odd. Why doesn't nature just make larger particles, instead of building atoms up out of small ones? Why not just have larger and larger atoms, instead of building molecules up from combinations of atoms? For that matter, why

are *you* composed of many billions of cells instead of being one super-giant-sized cell?

Systems and Stability

It seems that the reason in every case is that a collection of smaller units—a system—is more *stable* than one large unit. For example, protons and neutrons are the largest particles that exist in nature. Physicists have made bigger particles experimentally, but these are so unstable that many of them last less than a billionth of a second before they disintegrate. Similarly, atoms bigger than a certain size become more and more unstable. (Uranium, the heaviest natural element, is radioactive because its atoms are constantly breaking down into smaller, more stable elements; a process which gives off radiation. Man-made elements like plutonium, which are even heavier than uranium, are

Universe

Galaxy

Solar System

Planet Earth

World Ecosystem

World Civilization

Nation

State

Local Community

Individual (YOU!)

Nervous System

Brain

Brain Cell

Cell Nucleus

Molecule

Atom

Particle

Increasing Size →

even more unstable.) A cell larger than a certain size would simply die of suffocation, unable to move oxygen and food in, or waste products out, fast enough to stay alive.

The same thing is obviously true of the maximum size of animals: anything much bigger than a whale or a dinosaur would have a hard time finding enough food to keep going, much less coordinating its entire bulk efficiently. And it is easy to see how this works with social organizations. A group of five people can work together as a single team,.but a group of five thousand people would find it almost impossible to get anything done without dividing up into smaller working groups and organizing some way of communicating between those groups. In other words, a group that big is just a disorganized crowd or mob unless one or more *higher levels of system organization* are created.

Furthermore, even if gigantic low-level systems were possible, it would still be *simpler* to use a series of higher levels. There are millions of possible molecules, but instead of millions of different kinds of atoms, nature needs only 92. And instead of 92 basic particles, there only have to be 3—protons, neutrons, and electrons. For a living organism, too, it is much simpler to carry the "blueprint" for a few basic kinds of cells and another blueprint for how those cells will fit together, than it would be to try to carry a blueprint for the entire organism. And it is obviously much simpler for a society to have one set of basic rules which apply to all families, for instance, than it would be for it to try to create completely different basic rules for each individual family.

Even if we accept the idea that systems of a particular level become unstable as they grow beyond a certain point, we still have not established why it is that a higher level of system organization can be any more stable. In fact, there is a good reason for this stability and it goes back to our original definition of what a system is. If you remember, it said that *a system is a collection of things which interact with each other to function as a whole.* The key word here is *"interact."* If one part has an effect on the rest of the system and the system as a whole has an effect on that one part, then a "circular" relationship—or "loop"—has been created.

For example, you and a bicycle together form a simple, two-part system. Combined, you can do things which neither you nor the bicycle can do separately. Furthermore, your actions have an influence on what the bicycle does and the behavior of the bicycle has an influence on your actions.

Now, the interesting thing about even such a simple system as this one is the way it creates stability out of a situation which would normally be very unstable. If you climb on the bike and do nothing, neither you nor the bike will stay upright for very long. In fact, if you climb on the bike and do the *wrong* things, you will still end up on the pavement with a thump.

What happens, when you ride a bicycle skillfully, is that you are constantly making small adjustments to correct for "errors" in the path and the balance of the bicycle. If the bicycle starts to turn or tilt one way, you shift your balance or steer in the other direction. If it goes too far the other way you nudge it back again, and so forth, thus keeping it upright and on course. In fact, even if it looks like you are riding in a straight line, you are actually making a constant series of wiggles from one side to the other as the bike moves slightly off course and you correct for it, over and over

WIND

"The rider is constantly making small adjustments"

again. Sometimes it is easier to see this pattern if you slow way down, or watch someone who is just learning to ride—in either case, the wiggles will be quite a bit larger. As you speed up or grow more skillful, your corrections become smoother and less obvious.

To ride a bike properly, you need information about where the bicycle is and which way it is tilting, information you get from your eyes, your muscles, and the balance tubes in your ears. Without a continuous flow of this information, you would find it difficult—if not impossible—to ride the bicycle at all. (Just think how hard it would be to ride a bicycle with your eyes shut!)

Here's how we could diagram such a system:

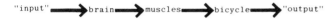

In other words, your brain tells your muscles what to do, your muscles push against the bicycle, and the bicycle responds by moving. The "input" is the information you had which caused you to decide to use your muscles the way you did, and the "output" of the system is the motion of the bicycle and yourself. But now, after you start the system moving, there's a new situation and a new position for the bicycle, which provides new information for your brain to work with. In other words, a new line should be added to our diagram:

In this way, information about the *output* of the system is *fed back* around to the *input* side of the system. Information that is used this way is called *"feedback,"* and any system like the one diagrammed above is called a "feedback loop."

Can you see now how this feedback provides stability in a system that would otherwise be unstable? Your brain receives information about where the bicycle is and compares that with where the bicycle *should* be. If there is a difference between the two for any reason—whether it's because you made a slight error or because the environment has changed—your brain tells your muscles the way you did and the "output" of the be eliminated, thus bringing the system back on course. Because this kind of system acts to cancel out or *"negate"* any changes in the system, it is called a *"negative feedback"* loop.* This idea of negative feedback seems simple but it is extremely important for understanding the systems in our environment. As we will see in the next two chapters, these negative feedback loops occur by the thousands inside us and all around us.

---

*Unfortunately, the phrase "negative feedback" is sometimes used loosely as a synonym for "criticism," particularly in education. When talking about *systems* try to keep in mind that *negative* feedback isn't necessarily good or bad. It is simply a process which *negates* changes or disturbances in the system.

Chapter Two:
STABILITY

The world around us is full of change. The physical environment on earth is one of continuous change in temperature, radiation, moisture, windspeed, and so on. Even the surface of the earth itself is constantly changing, with sea beds being thrust up to make mountains and mountains constantly being worn down again. Any system which is going to survive long enough to be an important part of our environment has to have the ability to cope with that kind of change and survive it. *All* stable systems get this self-stabilizing ability from negative feedback loops.

Negative feedback loops are everywhere, in every part of our natural and social environment. If we understand how they work, we will have a tool that will help us understand all kinds of systems.

The easiest way to get a feel for how negative feedback works is to look at a number of different examples from different kinds of systems, which is what we are going to do in the rest of this chapter. Then, in Chapter 3, we will have a look at some principles, or rules of thumb, which you can apply to all systems that have negative feedback.

The Thermostat: One of the most common mechanical feedback systems is the **heating** system found in most homes and buildings. Once a temperature has been set on the thermostat, the system will try to keep the temperature in the house as close to that level as possible. If the temperature drops below that level, the thermostat responds by turning the furnace on. The furnace produces heat, which warms the air back up. Eventually, the temperature rises above the desired level and the thermostat shuts the furnace off. Then, if it is colder outside than inside, the house will cool down again until the thermostat turns the furnace on, and the whole cycle is repeated. A diagram of the feedback loop looks like this:

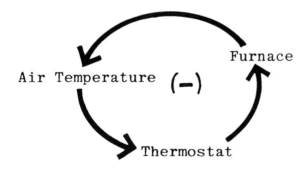

Following the arrows, this diagram says: "The furnace controls the air temperature, the air temperature controls the thermostat, and the thermostat controls the furnace." In addition, the minus sign in the middle tells us that this is a *negative* feedback loop, so that changes will be cancelled out—a drop in the air temperature will be followed by a *rise* in the air temperature, and a rise will be followed by a drop.

The nice thing about this system is that it responds *automatically* to changes in its environment. If it warms up outside, the thermostat shuts the furnace off and keeps it off as long as the air inside is at least as warm as it should be. If it cools down just a little outside, the house will cool off slowly and warm up quickly, so the thermostat will keep the furnace on for only a few minutes every hour, just enough to make up the difference. But as it gets really cold outside, the thermostat might have to keep the furnace running nearly all the time. The result is to keep the inside temperature stable, regardless of how the temperature outside drops.

What about hot days? A heating system can't do anything to keep a house cool, but at least the thermostat can shut the furnace off and keep it from making the house even hotter. Of course, we could add an air conditioner to the system and connect it to the thermostat. Now, if we set the heating system for 70 degrees and the cooling system for 78 degrees, the thermostat will turn the furnace on if the temperature drops below 70 degrees and the air conditioner on if it rises above 78 degrees. This changes a one-directional feedback system which keeps us from getting cold into a *two*-directional system which will keep the house comfortable in any weather.

Thermostats are cheap to make and save people a lot of effort, so they are found in many different places. Have you ever noticed how, if you open the door of the refrigerator when the motor is off, the motor usually starts up again after a few seconds? That's because opening the door lets warm air in and the *thermostat* inside the refrigerator senses the change in temperature. Thermostats keep the water in a water-heater hot and the water in a water-cooler cold. Thermostats are also found in electric stoves, in the cooling systems of automobiles, and in many other places.

Body Temperature: The thermostat in your house is a human invention, of course, but the *original* thermostat was invented by nature several hundred million years ago. To begin with, animals had no way to control the temperature of their own bodies. Many of the simpler animals, like the reptiles, are still like this. They can move fast when they are warm, but they slow way down when the weather gets cold, and they get overheated and die when the weather gets too hot. Over the years, however, some animals developed "thermostats" for keeping their body temperatures the same in spite of changes in the outside environment. Being "warm-blooded" was a big advantage, especially in cold weather, so these animals gradually developed more and more efficient systems for temperature control.

Human beings are warm-blooded, of course, and our temperature control systems are usually quite accurate. Most people have body thermostats that are set for around 98.6 degrees. If your body temperature starts to fall below that, your thermostat makes a number of things happen. First, it turns up your "furnace" causing you to burn fuel (food) faster, thus creating more heat. Then it will start you shivering, which makes your muscles work harder even when you are not doing anything, and that creates even more heat. And while these and other things are going on, your body sends a message to your brain saying, "I'm cold!" and you start looking around for hot food, heavier clothes, or a warmer location. Similarly, if you get too *hot,* you start to sweat, the blood vessels under the skin expand so that your blood can carry body heat to the surface more quickly, and you are likely to get a strong urge to slow down, loosen your clothes, and find a cold drink and a spot in the shade.

"It turns up your 'furnace,' thus creating heat."

Either way, the system keeps the temperature in the middle of your body nearly constant. Even when you *feel* so hot or cold that you can barely stand it, your body temperature rarely changes more than half a degree (unless you get sick). The feeling of being too hot or too cold is part of the feedback loop, and what it actually tells you is how hard your body is working to control its temperature. So when you say, "I'm cold!", what you really mean is, "My body is having to work too hard keeping me warm!"...and vice versa.

Float Valves: Another kind of simple, *self-regulating* machine was probably invented long ago by a farmer to keep a pond from either flooding or drying up. What this early genius did was to pivot a stick in the middle, fasten one end to a chunk of wood floating in his pond, and fasten the other end to the gate or valve which let water into the pond. Then, whenever the water level in the pond dropped, the float pulled one end of the stick down, which pulled the other end up, which opened the gate and let more water in.

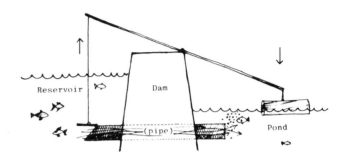

As the water rushed into the pond, it pushed the float up, allowing the gate to settle back into place, gradually shutting off the flow of water.

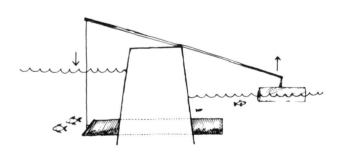

As the water evaporated or was used up, the water level dropped, and the whole cycle started all over again. The feedback diagram of the cycle looks like this:

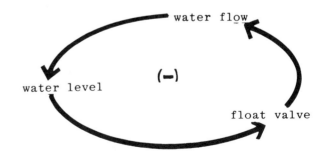

Like thermostats, float valves are simple, reliable, and cheap to make, and they save people a lot of time and hassle. As a result, they have found a lot of uses. There are more than a billion of them in use today in just two kinds of systems. One of these is the carburetor on most gasoline engines which uses a float valve to regulate the supply of gasoline. The other is the standard flush toilet which uses a float valve to control the water level in the tank.

(If you want to see how this works, carefully lift the lid off the tank and set it aside. The float is the large hollow ball on the right, fastened by a rod to the valve assembly on the left. When the toilet is flushed, water drains out of the tank and the float drops, which opens the valve and lets water in. As the water fills the tank, it lifts the float back up, until the float is high enough to shut off the valve again, and the system is ready for another flush.)

Thirst: People and other living things don't have float valves inside them, but they do have systems which control the amount of water inside them. Water is essential to life and it is constantly being used up to flush wastes out of the system and, for many plants and animals, to help with cooling. We are all familiar, of course, with the way this feedback loop works in human beings: when the water content of your body drops too low, you get thirsty! (Oddly enough, we don't have a similar word for the feeling which tells us to stop when we've drunk enough water, even though the feeling is unmistakable. Try drinking three straight glasses of water when you aren't at all thirsty—it really is quite unpleasant!) Even though the "pieces" of the thirst system are very different from the "pieces" that make up a float-valve system, the two systems do the same job using the same negative feedback loop arrangement:

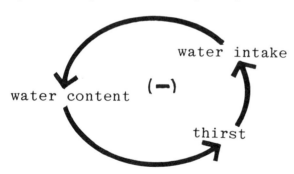

Inventories: The manager of a store faces a similar problem in controlling the supply of things he has for sale. He doesn't want to get stuck with boxes of stock which no one wants to buy, because that way he loses money. On the other hand, he doesn't want to run out of things that people want to buy, because then they will go to another store and he will lose money this way as well. So a good manager has to keep a very careful eye on his stock. If something sells more slowly than expected, he must quickly reduce or cancel his orders. If it is really unpopular, he may find that he has to reduce the price to get people to buy it. He might even have to sell it for less than he paid for it, just to get rid of it and make room for other things he can sell at a profit.

"He may find he has to reduce the price to get people to buy it."

On the other hand, if something proves more popular than expected, he has to place additional orders quickly before he runs out. If it is something that takes a long time to receive after it is ordered, and he realizes that he is going to run out anyhow, he may decide to *increase* the price so that fewer people will want to buy it. If he guesses right on how much to raise the price, his stock should just last until the new supply arrives. (In addition, of course, he will make more money on each item, which he can use to make up for the money he lost on other items which he had to put on sale.) Because the manager has the choice of adjusting either his orders or his prices, or both, the diagram here is a little more complicated:

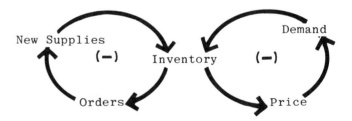

This is an example of a basic negative feedback relationship in economics. It is called the "law of supply and demand" because it works to keep a stable balance between the *supply* of something and the *demand* for it. If the supply is larger than the demand, the feedback cycles work to reduce the supply (cancelling orders) or increase the demand (by reducing the price), or both, until supply equals demand. And if the demand is greater than the supply, it works to reduce the demand (by increasing the price) or increase the supply (by placing new orders), or both, until the two are equal again.

8

Group Membership: A similar pair of feedback loops helps to maintain the stability of a lot of social organizations. For example, many kinds of social groups need some minimum number of members in order to function properly. A church needs a big enough congregation to pay the minister's salary and the upkeep on the church property. A P.T.A. needs enough members to serve on its committees and to meet with school administrators and school board members. A social club or a scout troop needs enough members so there will be plenty of people to have fun with. A basketball team needs enough players to keep at least 5 on the floor, even if some get hurt or winded or thrown out. And so on.

Any group like this has to recruit new members to replace those who die, move away, find other interests, or simply get bored and drop out. If the people wanting to join the group are enough to replace those who leave, there is no problem. But if more people quit than join, the size of the group will drop and the remaining members will begin to get worried. They may organize a membership drive, advertise their group, go out and try to talk people into joining, make the group easier to get into, or try to make membership in the group more appealing to new people. On the other hand, they might try to find out why old members are leaving the group so that they can reduce the drop-out rate. If either or both of these efforts are succcessful, the membership of the group will rise again until it is safely above the minimum level, at which point the special recruiting activities can be reduced. The result is a negative feedback process which keeps the number of new members joining the group approximately equal to the number of old members leaving the group, and which therefore keeps membership of the group approximately stable.

Predators and Prey: The examples above concern human communities, but the basic ideas apply to other kinds of communities as well. A natural *ecology* is a community of plants and animals, like a forest, a swamp, a meadow, or a lake. The relationships between the different living things in these natural communities are kept in balance by the same kinds of negative feedback loops which keep human communities stable. One of the most important of these loops is found in the relationship between predators (animals which eat other animals) and their prey (the animals they eat), and the way that this relationship keeps the populations of both the predators and the prey animals fairly stable.

For example, in some areas the deer and the wolf have a close relationship. If something happens (like an exceptionally cold winter) to reduce the number of deer in an area, the wolves will find it harder to find food. Old or injured wolves which might have survived will die, younger wolves will move out of the area to look for a better food supply, and many wolf cubs will die of hunger and disease.

But now there are fewer wolves for the deer to have to worry about, so many more of the young deer will survive than would have normally. When these deer grow up, there are more parents than normal, and these extra parents produce an even larger number of new fawns (baby deer). If the winter is mild and other conditions are good, this soon creates a rapid increase in the deer population. But, as the supply of deer increases, the wolves find it easier to catch food. Wolves which would have left or starved are now able to remain and stay healthy. Pretty soon, with so many wolves around, the deer find it a lot harder to keep from being caught. When the wolf population gets large enough, it actually begins reducing the deer population.

Eventually, with too many wolves and not enough deer, the wolves will begin starving again. This reduces the wolf population, which lets the deer population start growing again, and we are back where we started from. The result is a simple negative feedback loop which works like this: more deer means more wolves, which means fewer deer, which means fewer

NOW, OPEN UP AND SAY AHH

"The wolf is actually essential to the health of the deer"

wolves, which means more deer, which means more wolves, and so on.

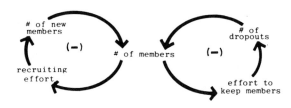

Incidentally, if you think this system is hard on the deer, it really isn't. The wolf is actually essential to the health of the deer population. If you went out and shot all of those "big bad wolves" the deer would soon be much worse off. For a while, their numbers would grow very rapidly, but sooner or later they would reach the point where there would be enough deer to eat up all of the food available in their environment. If this happened, an enormous number of deer would starve to death, and it might even wipe out the entire population.

Even if hunger were not a problem, disease would be. Normally, the wolves catch very few healthy, adult deer, but they do eliminate most of the animals that become sick. Without the wolves, the sick deer would pass their diseases along to the rest of the deer. If the population has grown to the point where the deer are quite crowded, the chances of one deer passing a disease along to another increases greatly, and it is possible for an epidemic to sweep through the entire deer population. The wolves prevent this by thinning the herd and killing off the sick ones before they can infect the others. So, strange as it may seem, eliminating the wolves would be bad for the deer!

The way in which this negative feedback process works may seem cruel, but the stability which it provides is essential to the well-being and survival of both the wolves and the deer. In fact, similar relationships exist which involve all living organisms and which give natural ecologies the stability people refer to when they talk about the "balance of nature."

Tracking Systems: So far we have been talking about systems which "aim" at a fixed "target." A heating system "aims" at whatever temperature is set on the thermostat. A social group "aims" at maintaining a membership level which is sufficient for its particular activities. But systems can also be set up to follow or "track" a *moving* target. In fact, the principle is really the same. The system gets feedback on how far it is from where it should be and uses the feedback to try to reduce the *difference*. It doesn't matter to the system whether the difference comes from a change in the system or a change in the target—it just senses a difference and tries to reduce it. For example, you can save energy by turning your household thermostat down five or ten degrees at night and turning it back up again

when you get up in the morning. The negative feedback loop in the heating system causes it to "follow" each change, down to the lower temperature during the night and up to the higher temperature during the day.

A similar system can be used to keep solar energy collectors aimed at the sun. Tracking collectors usually gather the sun's rays from a large area and focus it onto a smaller area. As the sun moves across the sky, the point at which its rays are focused gradually slips away from the target area. One common solution is to put a ring of "sensors" around the target area and hook them up so that when the sun hits a sensor on one side of the target, it causes the lens to shift in the *opposite* direction. In this way, the collector tracks the image of the sun across the sky throughout the day.

A thermostat or solar collector tracks its target rather slowly, but tracking systems can also be created which work much faster and more accurately than a human being could. The military used this approach during World War II to design radar-controlled anti-aircraft guns which could "lock onto" an enemy airplane and follow it at high speed. Similar aiming systems are now used in guided missiles and a variety of other weapons, as well as in more peaceful systems, such as the one which the astronauts use to link up to space vehicles. In fact, it is now possible to design very complex automated machines, and even whole automated factories, using high speed computers to control thousands of negative feedback loops at the same time.

The tracking systems which we have considered so far have one thing in common: someone has figured out a way to make the gadget do the entire job, without depending on constant human control. However, most tools and machines still require people to provide feedback and guidance for the system. As a general rule, we replace these human/mechanical systems with all-mechanical ones only when the job is so simple and repetitious (like controlling a furnace) that a reliable, inexpensive machine can do it, *or* when the job is so difficult that a human being cannot do it effectively (like tracking a high speed jet).

In a human/mechanical system, the human being usually takes the place of the control unit. For example, it is the rider, not the bicycle, which receives the information about the progress of the rider-bicycle system and decides what to do next. The same principle applies to all vehicles—cars, boats, planes, roller skates, surf boards, etc.—as well as other systems requiring "coordination," ranging from hitting a nail with a hammer or a baseball with a bat to eating with a fork or writing your name.

Most of these need no further discussion, since they all work the same way as the bicycle-rider system we have already analyzed. The person in charge starts the system moving and then guides it with a series of corrections to keep it following the desired path. But the system works so fast and so smoothly in some cases that it doesn't seem possible that there is time for the

"Try closing your eyes before the start of each swing."

negative feedback process to happen. If you swing a bat at a baseball, you don't stop every inch and measure the position of the bat and decide where it is going to go next; you just swing it, don't you? Even though it feels that way, high speed photographs and careful measurements have shown that you make dozens of tiny corrections with the muscles in your arm, wrist, and fingers in the fraction of a second it takes the bat to reach the ball.

If you doubt this—and it *is* a little hard to believe—try closing your eyes just before the start of each swing. You may hit the ball a few times, but the odds are that you will miss it much more often than you hit it. (That's why the coach is always saying, "Keep your eye on the ball!")

Tracking systems are also common in natural and social systems. A sunflower tracks the sun across the sky just like a solar collector, and a bat tracks a flying bug with the precision of a guided missile. Politicians quickly learn to track changes in public opinion if they want to be re-elected. Companies learn to track changes in public buying habits, or they go broke. And so on. In other words, tracking systems crop up wherever systems have to aim at a moving target rather than a steady one.

It may be helpful at this point to summarize the examples of negative feedback that we've discussed so far. The list below divides the examples into categories and suggests some other uses of negative feedback in each category. Don't worry about the ones you aren't familiar with; instead, see if you can work out the

feedback loops for the ones you do recognize, and try to think of additional examples in each category.

Mechanical Systems
Already mentioned: Thermostat, float valve, solar tracker, radar-controlled gun, space vehicles.
Other examples: Cruise-control on a car, automatic pilot on a plane, automatic frequency control (AFC) on FM radios, governor on a steam engine or other machine, ship stabilizers. Can you think of more?

Human/mechanical Systems
Mentioned: Vehicles, bat, hammer, writing, eating.
Others: All non-automatic tools and machines.

Biological Systems
Mentioned: Body thermostat, thirst/control of water content, sun tracking, bug catching.
Others: Breathing reflex (oxygen and CO_2), hunger, blood sugar, balance, pain avoidance, blood pressure, blinking, iris size, sleep, muscle-building, blood chemistry, healing. Can you suggest others?

Ecological Systems
Mentioned: Predator/prey, population/food, population/disease.
Others: Population/stress, plants/CO_2 balance, ecological succession (healing). See chapter 7 for more.

11

Social Systems

Mentioned: Group membership, supply and demand, politicians/public opinion; companies/buying habits.

Others: Friendship, football strategy, disaster relief, elections, markets, bankruptcy, independent courts, free press; see chapters 8 and 9 for more on economic and political systems.

These are just a *few* examples of the way that negative feedback provides stability in all kinds of systems and in all parts of our environment. Although change is all around us, the result of change is not chaos. The reason for this is that we are also surrounded by systems which are able to cope with change, using negative feedback to control it. There are many thousands of these self-stabilizing systems at work in your own body right now to keep you alive and functioning. Your blood alone contains hundreds of chemicals—oxygen, carbon dioxide, water, salts, sugars, enzymes, fats, minerals, hormones, etc.—*each of which is regulated by one or more loops. And other natural and social systems depend on negative feedback just as much for their survival.*

Chapter Three:
THINGS IN COMMON

Because negative feedback is so universal, it makes all sorts of different systems behave in certain similar ways. In this chapter, we are going to take a look at some of these so that you will have a better idea of what to look for when studying the systems around you.

Active Systems: One important thing about self-stabilizing systems is that they make an *active* response to change. They don't just sit there and ignore pressures on them. If you prop a bicycle up on its kickstand and a breeze comes along, the bicycle won't do anything by itself to increase its own stability. If the breeze gets strong enough, it knocks the bicycle over. If you are *riding* the bicycle, however, and a cross-wind comes up, you can simply lean into the wind, pushing *against* the pressure. Other active systems work the same way.

But an active response to change requires the use of energy. Sometimes a system gets the energy it needs from the same outside forces which are trying to change it. For example, the most common type of wind generator uses the power of the wind itself, pressing against the tail vane, to keep the wind generator facing into the wind.

Other kinds of systems get their energy from different places, and many of them are able to store a certain amount of energy for a while. For example, living systems draw energy from sunlight or food and store the energy for later use. Some mechanical systems can also store energy—like the gas in a gas tank or the electricity in a battery—while others can be plugged into a wall socket which connects to the electric company's storage system.

Almost all *living* systems are also active in another important sense: they continue to function and to use energy even when they do not need to respond to their environments. Mechanical systems, like a car or a furnace, can be switched completely off for a while and then turned back on again. The same is true of some very simple living things. Some plant seeds can wait for decades for the right conditions to start growing and some microscopic animals can be frozen solid and then be brought back to life.

But most living things *must* stay active; if they ever completely stop, they die. When you sleep, it is like letting a motor idle, not like switching it off. Your heart still beats, you breathe, your stomach digests food, your muscles move, your cells perform their complex chemical tasks, and your brain keeps up constant electrical activity. And when you are awake, a lack of stimulation from your environment will soon make you feel bored enough to *actively seek or create* some kind of stimulus.

As a general rule, the more complex a system is, the more energy it must spend just to maintain itself and the more active it will be about initiating changes in its environment. A worm uses more energy for maintenance than a cabbage, a frog uses more than a worm, and a cat uses more than a frog. The cat is also much more active in seeking and creating stimulation, spending a great deal of energy on satisfying its curiosity and on play activities.

Is the same thing true of social systems? It seems to be. Just compare the economy of an isolated peasant community, where everyone keeps track of his own affairs, and a modern economy, with its banks, bookkeepers, accountants, computers, contracts, lawyers, corporations, stock markets, and its profusion of "frivolous" and playful products and services. Or compare a large national government with the political structure of a neighborhood club. In both cases, the more complex system has to spend a higher proportion of its energies on processing information and maintaining itself, and it generally has a higher level of internal activity (compared with its environment) than the simpler system. A club can even stop functioning for a while and start back up again, while a society obviously has to keep going all the time.

System Limitations: There are limits to the amount and kind of change which any active system can deal with. One kind of system failure occurs when a heavy stress on a system continues for a long time and the system's reserves are exhausted. For example, you store up energy in your body and then use it gradually over a period of time. If you are in a cold place, your body will use that energy to keep your body temperature up. But if you stay out in the cold too long, all of your energy reserves will be used up and your temperature control system will simply stop working. Even though you are cold, you will stop shivering and feel warm, but you will soon lose consciousness and die if you are not warmed up quickly. This is what happens when people die of "exposure."

Similarly, your body temperature will stay stable even when the air gets extremely hot...but only for a while. When that limit is passed, your temperature control system quits, you *stop* sweating, and your body temperature soars. This is called "heat-stroke" and it is fatal unless immediate steps are taken to cool you off. Many negative feedback systems are like this; they are very stable over a wide range of conditions, but fail abruptly when pushed beyond their limits, so it is important for us to learn what those limits are.

Loose Systems: Another characteristic of self-stabilizing systems is that negative feedback does not *prevent* change. It just responds to change and keeps it under control. The result is that characteristic "wobble" in the system's behavior, as the system moves away from its target condition, pulls itself back, moves away again, pulls itself back and so forth. In some cases, the

We all Know "Doormats"

wobbles are so small that they are hard to detect, but they are always there. In other cases, they are large enough to be obvious at a glance, giving these systems a loose or even "sloppy" appearance.

Loose systems are not necessarily bad; they are often cheaper and sturdier and better able to cope with large changes in the environment than more precise systems. For example, an ordinary thermostat can keep the temperature in a house from changing more than 5 or 6 degrees and costs around $30, but a super-accurate system which can keep the temperature of a special laboratory from changing more than a tenth of a degree costs more than $100,000.

Another example is one you can demonstrate for yourself in just a few moments. First, trace a circle on a piece of paper. Then find a pair of scissors and cut the circle out. Sooner or later, as you cut, you will see the scissors slipping away from the line you are trying to follow. Naturally, when this happens, you guide the scissors back again toward the line, and so on, with each change of direction leaving a bit too much or too little paper along the edge of the circle. As long as you don't mind a certain amount of this roughness you can cut the circle out quite quickly and easily. But if you decide that you want an extremely precise job done, you will find that it takes much more time, effort, and concentration. Even then, if you examine the edges of the circle carefully when you are finished, you will find that there are still tiny points and flat spots around the rim of the circle.

Sometimes the attempt to make a loose system more rigid or precise does much more harm than it is worth. For example, even the closest friendship is never perfectly harmonious. Occasional conflicts are inevitable, but not fatal, as long as the friends are willing to find ways to adapt to each other. But we all know of "doormats"—people who try too hard to

please. Because they can't stand even a slight conflict, they back down at the first sign of disagreement, disguise their own feelings, and let other people walk all over them. In short, they try to eliminate conflict by adapting "perfectly" to others and the usual result is to make their friendship not worth having.

Can you think of any other examples? How about the way we handle crime in our society? As it is now, we wait until after a crime has been committed, and then try to catch and punish the criminal, hoping the fear of punishment will keep most people from committing crimes.

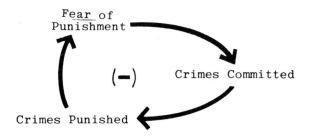

Wouldn't it be better to *prevent* all crimes from happening in the first place? But in order to do this we would have to have some way of watching each person in the society all the time. The cost would be ridiculous, and most people would object very strongly to the loss of privacy.

This does not mean that there aren't any negative feedback loops that could be made more accurate, because of course there are. But there are many more cases of systems which appear to be loose or sloppy but are actually functioning in the most efficient way. In either case, the negative feedback loop leaves its "signature" in the pattern of change/ response/ change/response....over and over again. Any time you spot this kind of cyclical or zig-zag behavior in a system, you can be almost sure that there is a negative feedback loop behind it.

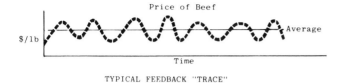

TYPICAL FEEDBACK "TRACE"

Reaction Times: Every negative feedback loop also has certain *time limits* which affect its behavior. One of the most important of these is the "reaction time," which is the minimum amount of time necessary for one complete circuit around the loop. Suppose, for example, someone sticks a pin in your arm. The reaction time, in this case, would be however long it takes for the pain to register, for the reaction signal to reach your muscles, and for the muscles to move your arm away from the pin.

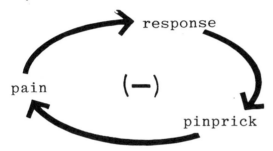

The reaction time for a simple pain reflex is quite short, taking only a few tenths of a second. Something more complicated and less urgent—like reacting to a street sign—takes longer because it requires conscious thought. Some mechanical systems, particularly electronic ones, have very quick reaction times, but others are quite slow. The basic thermostat/furnace cycle, for example, takes quite a while, because of the slow rate at which the air carries heat from the furnace to the thermostat. And social systems, in general, tend to have long reaction times. A company may take weeks or months to react to changes in buying patterns, while the political process often takes months or years to react to a change in the political situation.

Reaction time is important. If it is too slow, change can occur so fast that the system is damaged before it has a chance to respond. In addition, the reaction time is usually the same as the basic tempo or "beat" of a system— the minimum interval between the "wobbles" of the feedback cycle. So, by watching these wobbles and estimating that interval, you can frequently find out the minimum time period (and thus the fastest change) which a particular system can cope with.

Anticipation: Sometimes a system can't afford the delay that even a fast-reacting feedback loop involves. If the problem is a mosquito, you can ignore it until you feel it start to bite, and then react to it. (Smack!) But if the problem is a man-eating tiger, you had better find some way to respond *before* it bites, or even the fastest reaction time won't save you!

Systems cope with problems like this by reacting to *warnings*—events that usually happen before a particular problem occurs. Before a tiger attacks, you will usually see it, hear it, or smell it and have a chance to run or hide. This is still a negative feedback loop, and

"Systems cope with problems by reacting to warnings"

your reaction time is still important, but the loop is based on the warning signal rather than the actual problem:

The reaction time in the first loop has three parts: the time it takes the pain signal to travel up the nerves after the bite starts, the time it takes to choose and send a response signal, and the time it takes to swat the mosquito and stop the bite. The reaction time in the second loop also has three parts—from the start of the danger to an awareness of it, from awareness to the decision on how to respond, and from the decision to the end of the action that eliminates the danger—but the *first* part has become much more important. It helps if you can think fast and run fast, but that won't do you any good if your senses don't warn you of the danger in time.

Being able to anticipate dangers depends for most animals on sight, smell, hearing, *and the ability to interpret the information from these senses*. These traits are so useful for avoiding danger, as well as for finding food and mates, that evolution (see Chapter 7) has selected steadily for better and better senses and brains. (Of the two, better brains are somewhat more important than better senses: it does no good to have super-sharp ears if you can't tell that a tiger's cough means danger.)

The same process can also be used to improve the stability of social systems. If a country waits until it is attacked before it mobilizes its defenses, it is in bad trouble. If it regularly collects information about other countries, however, it can prepare its defenses in response to the *warning* that another country is getting ready to attack. If farmers wait for the fall rains to begin before they start to harvest, most of their crops will be ruined. But if they respond instead to a *forecast* of bad weather ahead, they can get their crops in before the rain starts. Similarly, if slide-rule makers wait until they are fired to start learning a new trade, they will likely have a difficult time. But if they see that pocket calculators are going to wipe out the slide-rule market, they can start looking around for a new trade while they still have plenty of time left to make the change.

To look at it from another point of view, one reason many systems have inadequate reaction times is that they have negative feedback loops which respond to problems rather than adequate warnings of those problems. This is especially true of political systems, particularly (as we will see in chapter 10) when the political system intervenes in the economic and ecological systems. The failure to build greater foresight into our social systems is in many ways the most dangerous and most serious limit we face.

"Counter-Intuitive" Systems: Negative feedback often produces behavior which appears contrary to common sense, or "counter-intuitive." We saw one example of this in the predator-prey relationship, where killing the deer's enemy (the wolf) was actually harmful to the deer. A similar situation occurs when a farmer tries to kill off a pest. Most insect pests have predators which keep them under control naturally. Unfortunately, most pesticides kill the predators as well as the pests. Since the pests usually breed faster than the predators, this means that the next generation of pests will arrive and there will be no predators there to control them. The result is a pest "explosion," and the farmer is worse off than he was when he started.

There are many other situations where a solution to a problem seems "obvious," but either doesn't work or actually does harm because of the way the system tries to cancel out the interference. For instance, most of us take for granted that there will be enough housing for us to find shelter, though we may pay more for it than we wish. But suppose that many people decided at the same time to move to a particular city. Suddenly, there will be many extra people looking for places to live and not enough houses and apartments to go around. Landlords will find that they can raise rents and still rent all their units. This makes apartment buildings more profitable, so people rush to build new ones and fix old ones up instead of letting them fall apart. For a short while, rents are high, which is unpleasant, but this leads to an increase in the *supply,* which solves the basic shortage and helps bring rents down again.

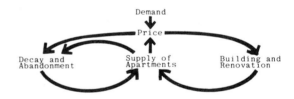

However, in some cities, the people looked at only the short-term problem—high rents—and demanded that government "do something." So the government did the "obvious" thing and passed laws limiting the rents landlords could charge. This, they thought, would surely lower the price of housing.

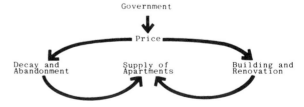

In the *short-run,* the rent controls did make housing cheaper. However, landlords found that they could not charge more rent in order to keep buildings in repair, so they either let the buildings run down, or they sold them and moved their business elsewhere.

Gradually, buildings decayed. Moreover, builders were not interested in constructing new housing units, because they were afraid that with rent control, they could not make enough to pay back their investment and to make up for the risk they took in building large developments. As a result, although housing was decaying, less new housing was constructed. There were fewer and fewer apartments available, and the price of those not controlled began to rise because of the scarcity. *Over the long run,* the city with rent control found that it had *less* housing for its citizens—and that the housing was *more* expensive and of lower quality!

Here is another example. High blood pressure is a serious problem which affects millions of people. Normally, blood pressure is controlled by a negative feedback loop which has an adjustable setting. When you are afraid, for instance, your body produces chemicals which raise the "target" of this "pressure-stat", just like increasing the temperature setting on a thermostat, and your blood pressure goes up accordingly. When you relax, the target is lowered again and your blood pressure drops back to a safer level.

Sometimes, however, the "pressure-stat" gets stuck at the higher setting for some reason, perhaps because a person is under too much stress or consumes too much salt or coffee or has something wrong with his body chemistry. When this happens, the problem can be solved by eliminating the cause and/or by taking drugs which push the "pressure-stat" setting back down again.

But it turns out that the body also has several other systems which affect blood pressure. One of these involves the kidneys, which filter waste products out of the blood. If enough blood isn't reaching your kidneys, these wastes build up in the blood and poison you. To keep that from happening, the body has a backup system which raises the blood pressure whenever the level of waste in the blood gets too high.

Consider what happens if something partly blocks the arteries that carry blood to your kidneys. The effect is like putting a kink in a garden hose—the flow below the kink drops to a trickle. Your body reacts to this in the only way it can, by pushing the blood pressure setting higher and trying to *force* more blood past the blockage. Of course, this means that the blood pressure everywhere else goes up too, which causes other problems, but at least it keeps you alive.

Now see if you can figure out what will happen if you go to a doctor for help. Since the problem is high blood pressure, the "obvious" solution is to give you one of the drugs that reduce blood pressure. The medicine causes your blood pressure to drop, which reduces the flow to the kidneys, which lets wastes accumulate in your blood, which makes your blood pressure go right back up again! If the doctor gives you a slightly stronger dose of the medicine, your body just fights back a bit harder. Pretty soon, if the doctor gets stubborn, you are caught in a tug-of-war between the drug and your kidneys— and if the drug wins, you die

of blood poisoning! (For your sake, however, let's hope the doctor is enough of a systems thinker to find the real solution: surgery to remove the kink in the kidney arteries.)

Again, the pattern is the same: *the "obvious" solution doesn't work* because the negative feedback loop is set up to cancel out any direct interventions. In fact, as we have seen, the "obvious" solution often makes things worse. *If you want to change a situation which is controlled by a negative feedback loop, it is much better to try to change the way the pieces interact than to try to "out-muscle" the system.* But that means that you *first* have to figure out what the system is and how it works.

Hidden Systems: Even if you understand how negative feedback works, it is often hard to guess how a system will react to a change because the feedback loops you need to know about are seldom out in plain sight. For example, the villagers in one region of Africa had trouble with hippopotamuses coming up from the river to eat up the villager's gardens. But when they killed off the hippos, many of the villagers got sick. Nobody could understand why, until a local scientist finally discovered the connection. The disease was caused by an organism which bred in the mud along the river. When the hippopotamuses churned up the mud, they killed most of the eggs and kept the organism under control.

"The 'obvious' solution often makes things worse."

With the hippopotamuses gone, the organism could breed freely—with disastrous effects on the health of the villagers.

Another example—one that harmed hundreds of millions of people—occurred in the United States in 1929, when Congress decided to pass a set of heavy tariffs (or taxes) on products being brought into the United States. Investors began selling their shares in companies that depended—directly or indirectly—on imports or exports. This helped trigger the terrible stock market crash of that year. Yet no one at the time seems to have realized that there was a connection between the two events, even though the stories ran side-by-side on the front pages of many newspapers. If the tariff act really did trigger the crash, it might well have been one of the worst decisions in history, since the stock market crash led to the Great Depression, which helped Hitler come to power in Germany, which led directly to World War II. Hidden system-linkages like this one connecting free trade to economic stability—are worth searching out, even if they are sometimes hard to find.

Vulnerable Systems: Even the most stubborn negative feedback system is usually vulnerable to things which interfere with the way information is passed along in the feedback loop. For example, a breeze so weak that you would hardly notice it might still be able to knock you off your bicycle if it blew smoke or dust in your eyes. By making you shut your eyes, the breeze reduces the flow of information to your brain and easily disrupts the system, even though it doesn't have the strength to "out-muscle" the system. Similarly, nerve poisons are the deadliest kind because they attack the body's communication system. And any attempt to censor the press is dangerous to a democracy for essentially the same reason: it disrupts the flow of information which people need to make intelligent decisions.

However, sometimes this vulnerability can be used to good advantage when you *want* to change the way a system is acting. If obvious solutions don't work, it is often worthwhile to search for the negative feedback loops that are causing the trouble and try to find an indirect way to change their behavior.

For example, if you want to cool off an overheated house on a winter day the "obvious" solution is to open a window. But as soon as the temperature drops a few degrees below the thermostat setting, the furnace comes on full-blast, and all you do is waste a lot of energy. If it is cold enough outside, you might actually succeed in cooling the house this way—if you don't mind having the furnace on all the time—but it would be much more sensible to just change the setting on the thermostat.

However, suppose that for some reason you *can't* change the thermostat setting. You might decide instead to put a small heater—like a light bulb—right underneath the thermostat. The extra heat from this heater would "fool" the thermostat into thinking that the house is hotter than it really is, which would cause it to turn the furnace off, letting the house cool down. In other words, adding heat to the system (at the right point) can actually make it cooler! Sounds crazy, doesn't it?

Now suppose you stuck an ice pack on the thermostat instead of putting a heater under it—what would happen? The thermostat would feel the cold air from the ice pack and "think" that the house was too cold. As a result, it would turn the furnace on, making the house even hotter. So adding heat can make the system cooler, and adding ice can make the system hotter! Crazier and crazier!

The farmer can use a similar approach to solve his problems with pests eating his crops. When he tries to poison the pests, he also poisons their predators and ends up with a worse pest problem than ever. What would a "systems solution" to this problem be? One answer that a lot of people are experimenting with is to control the pests *indirectly* by increasing the number of predators. One way this can be done is to build bird houses for the kinds of birds which eat this particular type of pest. Another approach which some people use is to collect praying mantises and ladybugs and put them in their gardens or greenhouses. These two insects eat many of the other kinds of insects which do a lot of damage to vegetables and other plants.

Similar solutions show up in many other situations, and we will have a chance to look at some of these in later chapters. But by this point you should be getting an idea of *why* a systems approach to problems is so important. Without it, people who try to solve problems or improve things, frequently pick a "solution" that doesn't work or that backfires by making the situation worse. Since their solution looks reasonable, and they can't understand *why* it won't work, they usually respond by trying even harder.

Eventually, they get tired, frustrated, and angry, and they often end up deciding that the system itself is basically evil or that there is some kind of conspiracy to keep anybody from improving it.

System thinkers, on the other hand, realize from the beginning that all stable systems have, by definition, ways of resisting change. Instead of stubbornly fighting against the, system, they study it carefully to find out where the negative feedback loops are, how they work, and where they are vulnerable. A *system* solution may be quite indirect and difficult for other people to understand, but it is more likely to work, and that is much more satisfying.

"It would be more sensible
to change the thermostat"

Chapter Four:
CHANGE AND GROWTH

Negative feedback loops provide stability for the systems in our environment. How then do change and growth occur? Some change occurs when a negative feedback loop breaks down, such as when a person gets heatstroke or when a social system becomes unstable and collapses. Some change results from the feedback loops themselves, as they try to adapt to changes in other parts of their environment. And some of it clearly comes from chance events, such as a new mutation, or the winning of a million dollar lottery, or the eruption of a volcano. But a great deal of change going on around us comes from a completely different kind of feedback process, called *positive feedback*.

Feedback occurs when a change in one part of a system produces changes in the whole system which then "feed back" through the system and affect the original part again. *Negative* feedback works to cancel out, or negate, changes. The system "corrects" changes in its parts. When one part of the system gets "off target," the negative feedback loop provides adjustments to bring it back. But what happens if the feedback loop does just the opposite, and each change feeds back through the system to cause *more* change? The new change will cause still more changes, and so on, until something breaks the cycle. This is called *"positive feedback"* because it amplifies or *adds to* any disturbance in the system.

Have you ever been in a concert or lecture hall when the public address system suddenly let loose with an ear-splitting "SQUAAWWK"? This is caused by the accidental creation of a positive feedback loop. The microphone picks up sounds which it converts to an electrical signal. This signal is then multiplied in strength by the amplifier and used to drive a loudspeaker, which converts the signal back to sound again. The sound then spreads out again from the loudspeaker, losing strength as it goes. Some of this

sound may reach the microphone. If this *amplified* sound is stronger when it hits the microphone than the original sound which caused it, the microphone will send a still stronger signal to the amplifier. The amplifier will increase it more, and the loudspeaker will change it back into sound again. Then the new noise from the loudspeaker hits the microphone with still greater intensity. For each additional trip through the system, the noise is multiplied again until the loudspeaker is making as much noise as it possibly can. Each sound—fed back into the system—is a signal for the system to produce more.

Sound and electricity both move so quickly that a signal can travel around this positive feedback loop thousands of times in a second, picking up volume each time around. The noise seems to reach full volume almost instantly. Once it does, that "SQUAAWWK" would continue until someone intervened or the equipment broke down. To stop it, you have to break the feedback loop. You don't have to turn the amplifier down. You can just interrupt the feedback by muffling the microphone with your hand, or by moving the microphone further away from the speaker. Anything that cuts down the sound reaching the microphone, so that it is less than on the previous cycle, lets the noise fade away.

Money: Although it works much more slowly than a sound amplifier, a savings account functions like a "money amplifier," by means of a positive feedback loop. Suppose that you have $1000 to put in the bank, and the bank pays you 5% interest each year. Since 5% of $1000 is $50, at the end of the first year you will have your $1000, plus $50 more, for a total of $1050. If you leave this money in the bank for a second year, you will earn 5% of $1050, which is $52.50, and at the end of the year you will have $1050 + $52.50, or $1,102.50 The third year, the money will earn 5% of $1,102.50, or

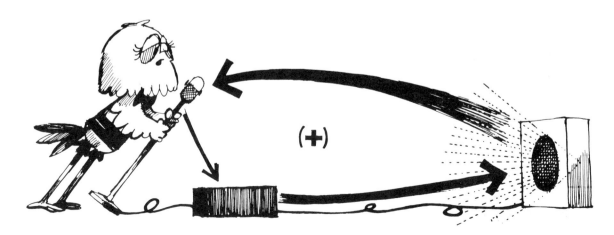

$55.13, for a total of $1,157.63. The table below shows how the interest grows, year after year.

Year	Interest Earned	Total in Account
1	$50	$1,050
2	52.50	1,102.50
3	55.13	1,157.63
4	57.88	1,215.51
5	60.77	1,276.28
6	63.81	1,340.09
7	67.00	1,407.10
8	70.36	1,477.46
9	73.87	1,551.33
10	77.57	1,628.89
11	81.44	1,710.34
12	85.52	1,795.86
13	89.79	1,885.65
14	94.28	1,979.93
15	99.00	2,078.93

As you can see, this process nearly *doubles your money*—from $1,000 to $2,000 in just 14 years. The money will double *again* in the next 14 years—from $2,000 to $4,000—and again for each 14 year period. The first time the interest is "fed back" around the loop, it adds only a small amount to the bank account. With each additional trip around the loop, a larger and larger amount is added. The positive feedback process *amplifies* the change.

An entire national economy can grow in this way. Farms, mines, factories, and businesses constantly create wealth, turning less valuable things into more valuable things. Instead of *consuming* all of the wealth they produce, people can *invest* some of it each year, using it to create more farms, mines, factories, and businesses, or to make the existing ones bigger or more efficient. Then even more wealth can be created the following year. Since more wealth is being produced, more can be invested. The additional investment makes it possible to create still more wealth, which lets people invest even more, and so on. Once again, positive feedback is at work—this time amplifying society's wealth.

Living Things: Simple one-celled organisms, like bacteria, may be able to divide as often as every half hour under favorable conditions. If you start off with a single cell, it divides and becomes two separate cells. After half an hour, each of these cells divides, producing four new cells. After another half hour, these divide again to create eight cells, which divide again to make 16, and again to make 32, 64, 128, and so on, doubling the number every half hour. Believe it or not, you would have more than one million cells after only 10 hours, and in just one day there would be more than 280 *trillion* bacteria—all produced from that same original cell!

All living things use this system to grow. Like almost all animals (and plants), you started out as a single fertilized cell, which divide into two, divided again into four, and kept on dividing. Unlike bacteria, however, your cells clung together in a clump instead of going their separate ways. Soon the cells in different parts of the growing clump began to assume different roles, some of them becoming skin cells, some becoming muscle cells, and some becoming nerve cells. Fortunately, each cell is also pre-programmed to stop dividing when it reaches a certain condition. Otherwise you would have kept on growing faster and faster until it killed you. (This is what happens when people get cancer: some of their cells lose the "stop dividing" signal, allowing the positive feedback process to start up again. Cancer cells then keep doubling, and grow out of control until they choke or destroy some vital part of the body.)

When we look at the next higher level of living systems, we find that *species* grow the same way that individual cells and organisms grow. Let's take rabbits for an example. Suppose we have a bunch of rabbits including ten adult females. (The exact number of males doesn't matter). Let's assume, also, that each of these adult females has ten daughters who survive and grow up and are each able to produce ten more daughter rabbits. At this rate, there will be ten adult females in the first generation, one hundred in the second, one thousand in the third, ten thousand in the fourth, a hundred thousand in the fifth, and one million females in the sixth generation! Of course, conditions rarely allow this rate of growth to continue for even four or five generations, but when circumstances *do* permit it, the rabbit is able to use this positive feedback process to expand very rapidly.

For example, when someone was foolish enough to bring the first few rabbits to Australia some years ago, the rabbits found the environment very much to their liking. Within a decade or two, those few rabbits had become millions and had spread to every corner of that large continent...breeding like rabbits, indeed!

So far, we've looked at mechanical, economic, and biological systems which use positive feedback to amplify change. Are there any others? The answer is that there are many, many more examples of positive feedback that we could use. In fact, positive feedback loops are almost as common as negative feedback loops. Two other positive feedback loops—knowledge and power—are particularly important.

Knowledge: One of the positive loops that has had a big effect on the human race is the one controlling the growth of *knowledge*. Back in prehistoric times, knowledge accumulated very slowly. An individual learned some things about his environment by direct experience and learned other things from other members of his tribe. In his short life, he might learn a few new things worth passing on to others, like a new way to shape an axe or a better way to plant crops. But he had no way to measure precisely, no time to study

"..and had spread to every corner of that large continent."

things that didn't directly affect his survival, and no way to record what he learned. When he died, most of what he had learned died with him. Knowledge could be stored only in the frail human memory.

If very knowledgeable people died before teaching what they knew to people around them, information was lost, and the next generation ended up knowing less about its environment than its parents did. If everything went well, it might know more. In what must have been the normal situation, it usually ended up knowing just about the same amount, for old facts would be forgotten and new discoveries made. Over many thousands of years, the gains might outnumber the losses, but by a very small margin. An epidemic or famine could set knowledge back sharply at any time. So progress was painfully slow.

Gradually, however, enough knowledge accumulated that people could run their lives more efficiently. Inventions like fire, farming, and astronomy gave them protection from the world around them and a better food supply. The new knowledge brought changes that permitted still more knowledge to be sought. People had somewhat longer, calmer lives, so they could spend more time and effort learning about their world and passing their knowledge on to others. They preserved and enjoyed it in paintings and carvings in the huts and caves where they lived, and in tales and songs they performed and remembered.

Even so, the accumulation went on very slowly until the invention of writing, about 5,000 years ago. Here, finally, was a way for people to record their knowledge for future generations without having to pass it on by word of mouth. The advantages were enormous. No longer would information be unavoidably lost because someone died. No longer was it necessary for an individual to spend time teaching the knowledge directly to everyone who wanted to learn it. No longer did discoveries have to be put in an artistic form to be remembered. Writing provided a permanent record which could be used by anyone who knew how to read.

Writing greatly speeded up the process of accumulating knowledge. The development of techniques for precise measurement and calculation, especially the development of arithmetic and geometry, also made the process move faster. Increased knowledge also allowed people to produce food and wealth more efficiently, which allowed more people to spend time pursuing more knowledge.

Eventually, people discovered that they could learn more and learn faster if they went about learning in a systematic way, and they began to discover the best ways of doing this. The result is the process called *science,* which is really nothing but a set of guidelines for the most effective ways to investigate and understand the world around us. Some of its tools are logic, mathematics, statistics, and devices like microscopes and telescopes that let us see or measure things that we can't observe directly.

More important in the development of science, though, was a set of *beliefs*. Scientists believe that knowledge can be accumulated faster if all scientists follow certain rules. Scientists are supposed to be absolutely honest about what they see, they should write down what they learn and distribute it to other scientists, and they should test their theories by actual experiments and not just rely on the opinions of authorities.

Of course, science didn't develop all at once, and many problems still hindered the accumulation of knowledge. For one thing, there were many, many mistaken beliefs which were mixed in with the facts that were being recorded and passed on. For another, copying documents by hand was a very slow and expensive process, so information moved slowly and was still often lost if just a few copies were destroyed. For example, the great library at Alexandria in ancient Egypt was destroyed by fire, along with all its contents. Many of the books and scrolls and records that it contained were the only copies anywhere in the world. As a result, we know of many important writings from ancient Greece, Rome, and Egypt only by references to them in other writings.

In the 16th century, however, Johann Gutenberg developed a fairly simple and inexpensive method for printing many copies of the same book. This allowed knowledge to accumulate faster. It became harder for information to be lost once it had been printed in many copies and distributed, and it became much easier for a student to get access to the knowledge that did exist.

The result of all these developments has been a continual acceleration of the rate at which knowledge has accumulated. At first, it was gathered very, very slowly. Then the pace began to pick up gradually until, with the development of printing and modern science, it has turned into a knowledge explosion. And it turns out that the more knowledge you have, the easier it is to create new knowledge. If you are trying to invent the airplane, it helps if other people in the society know how to make engines and fuel. If you want to figure out how to start a new kind of business, it helps a great deal if the local library has dozens of books on starting new businesses.

Furthermore, the more knowledge you have, the better off your society is, and the more people it can support to spend their time looking for more knowledge. One figure that is widely quoted illustrates this very well: 90% of the scientists who have ever lived are alive and working today! In other words, even though you can't touch knowledge, or see it, it can still grow by positive feedback in the same way that rabbits and businesses grow.

The only limit to positive feedback here is that we eventually come to a point where there is so much information that we can't find the information that we need. Fortunately modern computers may hold the key to coping with this information explosion, by organizing the knowledge we have and retrieving what we need at a particular time much faster than we can do it with books and magazines and file cabinets. Since computers are also a product of the growth of knowledge, this too is just a further extension of the positive feedback process.

Power: Other important positive feedback loops can be less desirable, however. One of these is the positive feedback loop of power, which has created problems for people since before the beginning of civilization. A power growth-loop works like this: when an individual (or group) gains power in a society through wealth, violence, religion, politics, or any other means, he has the ability to harm or help other people. Those other people naturally wish to please the person who has the power, so that they can avoid harm and share in the rewards. Now the power-holder not only has the original source of power, he also has a group of people who are willing to do what he wishes, which gives him even more power to help or harm other people. As a

"At first, it was gathered very, very slowly. Then the pace began to pick up slowly until... it turned into a knowledge explosion."

"...even more people wish to please him, which gives him still more power."

this chapter were selected with a purpose. The growth of knowledge, the growth of population, the growth of economic wealth, and the growth of power are the greatest forces for change in modern life. The growth of knowledge, by enabling human beings to make their lives more secure, longer, and healthier, has helped feed the growth of population. The growth of wealth and the growth of knowledge are actually interdependent, for new knowledge—inventions and discoveries about the way the physical world works—has helped people put their money to work in ways never dreamed of before, and to produce wealth beyond the imagination of earlier peoples.

However, both wealth and knowledge can also contribute to power. Knowledge of physics and chemistry, and even the understanding of how human beings work, can all be used to give some people power over others—better weapons, better ways of manipulating people's minds. Together, the modern growth of power, wealth, knowledge, and population creates an unprecedented situation of rapid and continuous change. One of the basic challenges of our times is finding ways to control this headlong change.

Positive feedback loops also affect our lives in less general ways. The spread of a fire, a rumor, a chain letter, or an epidemic disease—all of these are the result of positive feedback, as are all chemical and nuclear chain reactions. What they all have in common is an *explosive* quality, whereby a tiny initial spark can quickly cause enormous results. They are also often dangerous. As a result positive feedback loops are usually kept under very tight control in both natural and social systems, as we will see in chapter five.

Reminder: "Negative feedback" loops *negate* change, creating stability. "Positive feedback" loops *amplify* or add to change. Don't get them confused with "bad feedback" and "good feedback" or with "criticism" and "praise". Both terms are widely misused, so you have to be careful. Just remember that whether feedback is considered positive or negative depends on what it does to *changes* in the system.

result, even more people will wish to please him by doing what he wants, which gives him still more power. If nothing is done to stop this process, the individual will eventually control the entire society. This, in fact, is what has happened throughout history when tyrants and dictators have taken control of societies. Perhaps the best examples in this century have been Hitler's Germany, Stalin's Russia, and Mao's China.

Because power can accumulate so rapidly, any society which is trying to avoid a dictatorship must find ways to control and restrain this positive feedback loop. In fact, democracy as we know it today is a direct result of a series of inventions (like free elections and independent judges and civilian control of the military) which people have learned through painful experience are necessary for controlling this tendency for power to accumulate in one place.

Summary:

The examples of positive feedback discussed in

"Positive feedback loops affect our lives... as the spread of an epidemic or a rumor."

Chapter Five:
PUTTING THE PIECES TOGETHER

Back at the beginning of this section, we discussed the origins of systems thinking. Originally, people thought that the best way to study a system was to find out what it was made of, so they studied these pieces. Gradually, they learned that it was just as important to understand how the pieces were organized, but they still thought that the organization of any one *kind* of system—such as a living thing, or an economy—was unique. Only in the last 50 years have people begun to realize that all complex systems have many things in common in the way they are organized, even though the "pieces" may be very, very different.

Plus and Minus: The organization of *every* complex system is built out of the same two simple elements that we have just been discussing: positive and negative feedback loops. If you can think of the atoms in your body as being the basic building-blocks of your body's *physical* content, for example, then positive and negative feedback loops make up the basic building-blocks of your body's *organizational* content. The same thing is true of all other kinds of systems.

This similarity gives us a powerful tool. Now that you understand the basic units of organization, you can hunt for them in any particular system and see the similarities between the way that system behaves and the way other systems behave. This means that you can apply your experiences with one system to another more easily, even if you have never encountered the other system before. It also means that once you understand how these basic building blocks go together in one case, you will be able to transfer that learning to other fields, instead of having to start all over again from nothing.

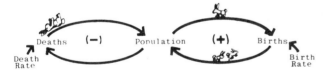

In this chapter, we are going to go a little further and examine the ways that different feedback loops can be linked together to build up more complex systems. Let's start with the simplest combination, using one feedback loop to each kind: When we were talking about population growth in chapter four—whether of rabbits or people or bacteria—we were discussing the "plus" loop of this system: the more rabbits there are, for example, the more offspring they can have; the more new rabbits are born, the more rabbits there will be, and so on. On the other hand, as the population of rabbits increases, the number of rabbits that die each year also increases. This is the *negative* loop in the diagram above.

These two loops work against each other. If ten rabbits are born and six rabbits die, the population

grows by four rabbits—the *difference* between the plus and minus loops. But if *twelve* rabbits die for every ten that are born, the population goes down. In other words, the actual behavior of the system depends upon which loop is "stronger". If the *birth rate* is higher, the population will grow; if the *death rate* is higher, the population will decline.

This isn't just limited to populations of rabbits, or people, or other living things. The same basic description applies to many other systems. For example, we saw that the growth of knowledge available to a society depended on the difference between the learning rate and the "forgetting rate." If more is learned than is forgotten, the supply of knowledge increases, and vice versa.

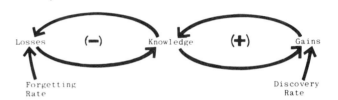

The same diagram can also be applied to economics. If a company takes in more money than it spends, it can grow, but if it spends more than it takes in, it will soon go broke. Another way of looking at the same thing, in terms of the whole society, is to think of our wealth-producing capacity ("capital")— farms, mines, factories, and businesses—as a *population*. If machines wear out (depreciate) faster than replacements are being made (investment), the ability of the society to produce more wealth will decline. On the other hand, if more capital is being produced than is destroyed each year, the wealth of that society will increase.

Multiple Loops: The next logical step is to ask what controls the *rate* at which the basic positive and negative feedback loops work. Let's go back to our population diagram, using rabbits again, and add on some loops. The first thing we want to ask is, what kinds of things could affect the death rate for rabbits? One thing is obviously the food supply. If there is plenty of food for each rabbit, there will be lots of sleek, healthy rabbits who will live a long time. On the other hand, if there is not enough food to go around, some rabbits will starve and others will be weakened by hunger and will be more likely to die for other reasons:

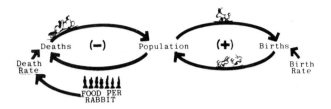

Now the two things that determine how much food there is per rabbit are the amount of food in a particular area and the number of rabbits in that same area:

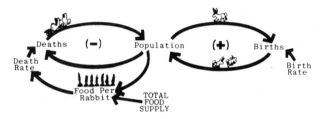

For the moment, let's assume that the amount of food is always the same. We now have an additional negative feedback loop: as the number of rabbits increases, the amount of food per rabbit decreases; as the amount of food per rabbit decreases, the death rate increases; and as the death rate increases, the number of rabbits goes back down again.

What are some of the other things that affect the death rate? Well, we've already talked about several possibilities back in Chapter 2, when we were talking about deer. Like deer, rabbits are affected by predators and disease. More rabbits means more predators, more predators means a higher death rate, and a higher death rate means fewer rabbits. Similarly, the more rabbits there are, the easier it is for a disease to spread rapidly and reduce the population. So let's add these two to our diagram.

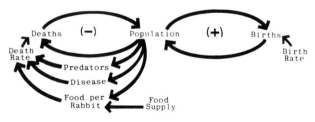

Have we missed anything? Suppose the population grows so much that the rabbits are really crowded together. It turns out that too much crowding produces stress, that stress stimulates the adrenalin glands, and that if the adrenalin glands are stimulated for too long the rabbits will just keel over and die from what the biologists call "shock." When they are in this condition, they will often go into convulsions and die at the slightest stimulus—a loud noise, the sight of an

enemy, or even the appearance of a handsome rabbit of the opposite sex. In effect, they literally die of fright or excitement. So, if all of the other negative feedback loops—including food, predators, and disease—should fail, the ultimate negative feedback loop is an internal one, triggered by overcrowding.

This last negative feedback loop is rarely used in nature because the others are so effective for most species. When it is used, however, the results can be spectacular. You have probably heard of the lemmings, small rodents in Scandinavia, which march into the sea and drown themselves by the millions approximately every four years. It turns out, after centuries of wrong guesses, that the real reason for this mass suicide is that the lemmings are driven crazy by periodic over-population and crowding. The snowshoe hares in northern North America also have a four year "boom/bust" cycle for the same reason.

Other animals use the amount of food or space available to control their population, but many do it by controlling the *birth rate*, instead of the death rate. For example, many types of birds will only mate, build nests, and lay eggs if they have a nesting space or territory of their own of at least a certain size. This doesn't affect the birth rate, as long as there is enough room for everybody, but when the population gets high enough so that the territories fill up all of the available space, then the left-over individuals—those without territories—will not produce any young.

This same tactic is used by a wide variety of other animals, including wolves, lions, and many other hunting animals. It is also the basic way in which plant populations are controlled. For instance, if trees in a particular area are thinly scattered, new seedlings have plenty of room and can get plenty of sunlight to grow. As they fill up the area, however, each tree blocks out the sun from the area around it until there is no more space for a new tree to get started.

So now we have additional feedback loops which affect both the birth rate and the death rate:

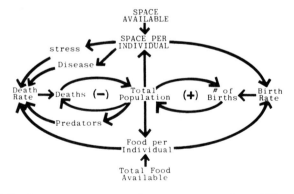

(*All* loops are negative, except the "Total Population/Number of Births" loop.)

The one that will eventually halt the growth of the population depends upon the particular situation.

Sometimes these negative feedback loops work together to control the positive feedback loop. More often, a few do the main job, and the rest are kept in reserve for the times when the few "normal" controls are not strong enough.

This pattern is common in many types of systems, and often leads to frustration for people who are unfamiliar with the way systems normally behave. As we will see in later chapters in Section II, people often intervene in a system to eliminate a negative feedback loop that they don't like, only to be surprised when a worse one takes its place. For example, if disease is reduced through better medicine *and nothing is done to limit the birth rate,* the human population then increases to the point where there is not enough food and a great famine occurs, killing even more people.

We've spent some time on this discussion of ways that a variety of negative feedback loops can limit the growth produced by a positive feedback loop because this is a very common combination in the world around us. Positive feedback is so powerful that it can produce incredible amounts of growth in a fairly short period of time. Many complex systems use this potential for rapid growth to allow them to react quickly to changes in the environment. At the same time, if it is allowed to go too far, it is almost always destructive and there will always be a limit somewhere, if only because of the fantastic numbers involved. (Rember the rabbits in Australia!) Most systems have therefore developed ways of stopping positive feedback after it has done its useful work, but *before* it reaches destructive levels. So one of the first things to look for in any complex system is the nature of the positive and negative feedback loops and the relationship between them. Generally speaking, the point at which the positive forces and the negative forces balance each other is the point the system will go back to, time after time, after being disturbed by some change in its environment.

This process of identifying the positive and negative loops is also important because it allows you to distinguish between things which are going to affect the system only temporarily, and things which are going to have a lasting effect. Essentially, *any change—no matter how big—which does not change the important positive and negative loops, will be only temporary.* At the same time, *any change—no matter how indirect or small it seems—which affects the relationship between the plus and the minus loops is going to alter the long-term behavior of the system.*

Competition: The examples above deal with combinations of many negative feedback loops, but only one positive one. What happens when a system has *more* than one positive loop? Actually, the population diagram on page 26 has two additional positive loops hidden in it: both the predators and the disease organisms increase by positive feedback whenever the rabbit population increases. From their point of view, an increase in the rabbit population means an increase in the available food supply, which relaxes one of the

negative feedback loops restraining their own growth.

Here's a diagram of how this works, using field mice and owls for our example this time:

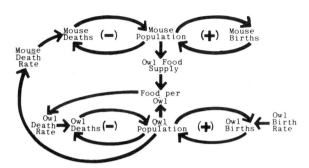

Positive feedback *increases* the field mouse population, which increases the owl food supply, which increases the food per owl, which reduces the owl death rate, which allows the owl population to grow, which increases the mouse death rate, which *reduces* the mouse population, which reduces the owl food supply, which increases the owl death rate and reduces the owl birthrate, which reduces the owl population, which.....etc. etc., etc.!

Or, more simply:

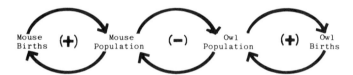

In other words, two positive feedback loops in competition with each other can provide stabilizing negative feedback for each other!

Competition is an important part of system design. Not only do predators and prey compete with each other for survival, but different predators also compete for the same prey. Foxes and owls for instance compete for food; more foxes means less food for owls and vice versa—and so on, with many competitors at each level, so that each helps control the population of the others.

In economics, companies limit each other by competition:

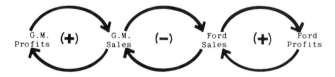

...and so on, for Chrysler, American Motors, Datsun, Toyota, Mercedes, Volkswagen (Rabbits again!) and all the others. Each company limits the other companies in two different ways: by actually taking sales away from the others and by forcing the others to keep prices down to keep from losing even more sales.

In politics, as we will see in Chapter 9, the competition is for *power,* competition between politicians, between political parties, between the branches of the government, and between the levels of the government. If one politician does a bad job of representing the people, his opponent will try to gain power by telling the people about it. If members of the party in power try to steal an election, the other party will be right there watching them, hoping to gain power by catching them at it. If Congress gets out of line, the President can veto its bills, and so on.

Knowledge is also managed in this way. Scientists and scholars compete for status and respect by trying to make new discoveries and develop new theories. If one scientist already has a good deal of prestige—perhaps he has won a Nobel prize—people will tend to accept what he says, even if it is wrong, which gives him still more power and prestige. But scientists also get prestige for discovering errors and disproving theories produced by other scientists. The result is that each scientist's efforts to increase his own prestige act as a check on the others' efforts. In the process, bad theories and false discoveries are weeded out, while good ones are encouraged.

A lot has been said in criticism of competition, and there is no doubt that it can be harmful if taken to extreme lengths. Owls instinctively want to catch all the mice they can, but if they actually *succeeded* in catching all the mice in a region they would soon be much worse off as a result, along with all of the other mouse predators. Society benefits a great deal from the competition between political parties as long as they fight fair, but the public would lose those benefits if one party decided to seize power illegally, or even if one party was so successful that it completely wiped out its competitors in fair elections. Similarly, business competition encourages innovation and helps keep prices down, but if one company is so successful that it drives all its competitors out of a particular field, then that company can raise its prices as much as it wants.

In other words, the kind of competition which one side completely "wins" is dangerous because it means *ending* the competition. However, real life is not a game, with a scoreboard, clock, and final score. Natural and social systems generally balance subsystems against each other in such a way that each will limit the others *without* winning a final victory that ends the competition.

This balancing process is dangerous, of course, since there is always a risk that a positive feedback loop will "break loose" and wreck the system. But positive feedback is so useful when rapid growth is needed that the risk is worth taking and all stable complex systems include growth loops surrounded by negative feedback loops to keep them under control. And since competition from other growth loops is the most effective form of control, most systems rely heavily on competition to keep things from blowing up.

The result of all this is a characteristic pattern that occurs in all but the simplest systems: a few powerful growth (+) loops balanced against each other and surrounded by swarms of stabilizing (-) loops which help keep them in balance. These two basic "pieces"—positive and negative feedback loops—can be put together in nearly an infinite number of ways, but the systems they make up have to follow this general pattern in order to survive. This is why successful systems, particularly complex systems, have the basic similarity of behavior which we will be discussing in chapter six.

Chapter Six:
COMPLEX SYSTEMS

Although many of the systems we have considered so far are, like the human body, obviously extremely complicated, we have treated them as though they were simple systems, or parts of simple systems. That is, we have considered them as elementary units in systems with only one or a few feedback loops. This does not necessarily mean we have over-simplified our descriptions of the systems we have considered. Even complicated systems, like nations, are sometimes parts of fairly simple systems composed of other nations, even though each of the parts is itself a very complicated system. Indeed, as you have probably realized already, components of systems in the real world are in fact members of thousands of larger systems, some of them simple, some not. Here we are going to consider some of the characteristics of what we will call *complex* systems, how they behave in ways different from simple systems, and some of the problems they present.

1. *Self-Stabilizing Systems:* The first characteristic of complex systems is that they can keep themselves stable in the face of a wide variety of environmental changes. To do this, complex systems need to contain great numbers of negative feedback loops and they need to be able to get and use a great deal of "information" about their environment. The very simplest systems—like a thermostat with a fixed temperature setting—have only one loop and need only one piece of information (like the room temperature) to do their jobs, but they can handle only *one* kind of change. The thermostat handles a cold night automatically, but there's not much it can do about

burglars or broken windows. Complex systems often contain thousands, even millions, of simple feedback loops so that they can "keep their balance" in spite of the many different kinds of changes that can happen in the real world.

2. *Goal-Seeking:* Another characteristic of complex systems is that they appear *purposeful*. That is, in addition to responding to their environments, they appear to have goals and to pursue those goals actively. In addition to surviving, living things "want" to produce offspring. Ecologies "want" to use every possible source of energy in the physical environment. Human beings want things like friendship, respect, security, and entertainment. Companies want to produce products and earn profits. It sounds perfectly all right when we talk this way about people, or social systems where the goals are chosen by people, but a little strange when we are talking about crabgrass "wanting" to produce more crabgrass. Nevertheless, non-human systems often are so persistent and ingenious about pursuing their "goals" that they *seem* to have minds of their own. Even human systems can appear to have their own goals, as when the economy "wants" rents to rise in a tight housing market, in spite of the fact that nearly all of the people *in* the economy want the rents to stay down.

3. *Program-following:* A third characteristic of systems is the ability to follow a "program" or sequence of steps, performing first one function, then another, then another, using feedback to decide when each step is completed. Cooking recipes provide a

"...The forks in the path, where choices between two or more options are present"

simple example: the cook is told to beat until fluffy, or bake until brown. When the egg whites are fluffy, or the cake is brown, the feedback loop is closed as the cook turns off the egg beater or oven and goes on to the next step.

A more complex type of program-following behavior is one that includes *branching*. Branching programs are used for decision-making in many ways, from medicine to auto repair, and they can be exceedingly simple or so complicated that a computer must be used to follow the steps. The forks in the path, where choices between two or more options are present, are what distinguish branching from simple program following. The doctor examining a patient may look first for fever. If there is a fever, he looks for a sore throat. If a sore throat is present, he might take a throat culture to find out what is causing the infection. If there is no fever, or no sore throat, he will follow up alternate lines of investigation until he finds the probable cause of the illness.

4. *Self-Reprogramming:* As systems become more complex, they generally acquire both the ability to follow more complex programs and the ability to *modify* those programs so as not to repeat errors. Bake until brown is a program a cook might follow once: one bitter experience may modify the program to "bake until brown, but not dark brown." A mouse may go down a lot of blind alleys while searching for cheese in a maze; after several trails, however, it will modify its search program and go directly to the cheese with few wrong turns. If a football play fails repeatedly, a smart coach will drop it from his program for the game.

Reprogramming to avoid repeating errors is one of the most basic forms of learning. Even a cockroach can do it to some extent. At the next level up, however, reprogramming means inventing new, better ways to achieve the old goal, and it begins to require a degree of insight and creativity. The football coach, for example, uses more complicated skills when he invents a new play that works than when he simply drops a play that fails.

5. *Anticipation:* This characteristic of complex systems, the ability to anticipate changes in the environment, was discussed at some length in chapter three. Anticipation is sometimes "wired into" the system, just as a fly is programmed to take off whenever something a certain size approaches at a certain speed, without having to be taught that such events mean danger.

In other cases, a system may learn by experience that one event usually precedes another one, and begin reacting to the first event in the way it reacts to the second. For example, if you ring a bell one minute before each time you feed your dog, the dog will learn to associate the two. Soon, it will start to salivate—that is, its mouth will literally start to water—whenever it hears the bell, even if there is no food around. Similarly, if a light flashes just before each time a rat is shocked, the rat will soon start jumping to

safety whenever the light comes on.

Finally, anticipation—like reprogramming—can be the result of insight, as when we figure out how some system is going to act in a particular situation even though we have never experienced that combination before. Have you ever heard a joke or seen a movie and been certain that a person you know would particularly like or dislike it? To do that fairly accurately, you have to have a pretty good model in your mind of how the person's "personality-system" works, and then be able to put the model and the situation together and watch the result in your imagination. The same kind of thing happens when an engineer looks at a drawing and visualizes how a machine will work, or a politician looks at a proposed new law and tries to guess what the public's reaction will be. Each requires a degree of *insight* into the new situation in order to anticipate the response.

6. *Environment Modifying:* As we have seen, systems can improve the efficiency with which they interact with their environment by modifying the programs they follow and by learning to anticipate changes. There is an alternative approach, however: they can modify the environment to make it easier to deal with. All systems have some effect on their environments, of course, but it is usually an accidental effect, and often even a harmful one. If cattle and sheep eat the grass in an area right down to the roots, turning grassland into desert, they are altering their environment, but in a way that is not good for cattle and sheep. On the other hand, when beavers are unable to find a suitable pond, they will build a dam across a stream and create a pond which they can live in, thus *improving* the environment from their own point of view.

Although many insects, birds, and other animals have programs for improving their environments, most of these are fairly simple path-making or nest-building programs. However, one animal—*Homo Sapiens*—has made a very successful specialty out of modifying its environment for a wide range of purposes. Farming alone has involved the physical remodeling of almost a quarter of the earth's land surface. Other activities, like mining, tree cutting, and the construction of things like buildings, roads, and airports, have also created enormous changes in both the physical and biological environment. These changes have often been harmful, as when plowing turns a prairie into a dust-bowl, or when tree-cutting causes floods and landslides, but *in general* this human pattern of changing the environment to suit our needs is what has made civilization possible.

7. *Self-Replicating:* Another characteristic of many complex systems is the ability of the systems to reproduce, or replicate, themselves. The most familiar examples of self-replicating systems are living organisms, which, through division or coupling with another organism, are able to produce copies of themselves. The process is so complex that it may never be fully

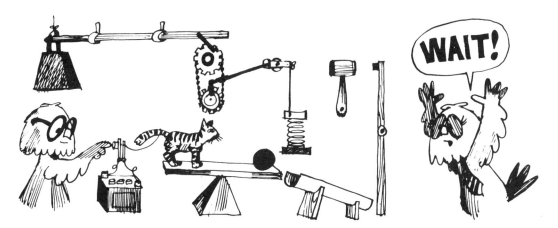

"...as when we figure out how some system is going to act even though we have never experienced that combination before."

analyzed, for it requires packing an incredible amount of program information into the nucleus of each reproductive cell. These instructions must specify exactly how and when to combine a few dozen chemical elements, such as carbon, hydrogen, oxygen, nitrogen, and calcium, into skin or bark; wood, bone, shell, horn or teeth; hemoglobin or chlorophyll; blood or sap; milk, mucus, sweat, or venom; tendons, muscle, or cartilage; and all of the other substances that make up a living thing.

Although biological reproduction is the most obvious example, self-replication can also occur among social systems, such as when a society sends out pioneers to found a new community, or the owner of one McDonald's franchise creates another one. An interesting thing to note in both cases, biological reproduction and the founding of new institutions, is that the child is rarely an exact duplicate of the parent. Apparently systems which can replicate themselves are also complex enough to modify their programs slightly in the process. As we will see in the next section, this flexibility can provide a big survival advantage.

8. *Self-Maintaining and Repairing:* Another form of systems behavior typical in biological and social systems and rare in machines is self-maintenance and repair. Like self-replication, self-maintenance requires a huge library of information packed in a small space, and the result is rarely more than a very close approximation of the original. For example, the cells in your body are constantly dying and being replaced by new cells. Even though this means that the system is constantly changing at the microscopic level, it also maintains the system as a whole and keeps it functioning. Similarly, if you cut yourself or break a bone, your body will try to repair the damage. If all goes well, the arrangement of cells when the healing is complete will be "close enough" to the original, but never precisely the same.

Social organizations also reveal this kind of behavior. In a city, for example, older buildings are constantly being torn down and new, different ones built to replace them. Even though, in one particular spot, a bowling alley might be torn down and replaced by an apartment building, the city as a whole will maintain approximately the same mixture of places for working, living, and recreation. And when a tornado or earthquake or other disaster destroys part of a town, the community will usually re-build itself in similar— but not identical—ways.

9. *Self-Reorganizing:* In addition to being able to maintain and repair themselves, some complex systems are capable of reorganizing themselves—actually rearranging their own parts and changing the connections between those parts—to meet new conditions or achieve new goals. This is easiest to see in social organizations, like a country that changes its form of government or a company that completely reorganizes the way it does business. However, many types of living systems are also capable of reorganizing themselves, even if not to the same extent. You can't grow gills or a tail, for example, but you can grow larger muscles, a larger heart, bigger lung capacity, and so on, in response to regular physical exercise.

In addition, the human mind has the very important ability to reorganize itself and its contents to a considerable extent. Most of us have had the experience, for example, of having bits of information that we've known for a while suddenly fit together to create a new picture of a situation. As we get older, we are constantly rearranging our memories in more efficient patterns, and even reorganizing our whole

WE ARE REORGANIZING OUR COMPLEX SOCIAL SYSTEM

DOES THIS MEAN I'M OUT OF OFFICE?

"It's easiest to see in social organizations like a country that changes its form of government."

personality system. When this happens slowly, we call it "maturing," but it sometimes happens very rapidly as the result of some personal crisis. A religious conversion, like the one experienced by Saul of Tarsus as described in the Christian Bible, is an example.

10. *Self-Programming:* Highly complex systems go beyond the beaver's simple selection among alternatives: to build or not to build a dam. They often appear to *invent* goals, not merely choose them according to some inherited program. A political system may pursue liberty over security, or justice over creativity, or honor over safety, or vice versa in each case. An economic system may choose opportunity over order, or predictability over fun. (Compare the Spartans and the Athenians, or the Puritans and the Polynesians.) They may do so without the conscious realization that those are the choices they are making.

After a new goal is invented, a new program must also be developed to achieve it, not always on the basis of pre-existing programs, but often on the basis of insight. This is typical of human activity when a new project, never before undertaken, is successfully pursued. There are no lessons of experience to follow; the program must be modified by insight. The Apollo moon landing is a conspicuous example.

These traits—the ability to invent new goals and the ability to devise new programs for achieving those goals—represent the highest level of flexibility in complex systems. Animals may demonstrate considerable ingenuity in solving problems, but the goals they pursue are essentially built-in, dictated by their genes. It could not occur to a wren to want to build cathedrals or to a pig to want to understand physics. Both goals can, however, occur to human beings and to human social systems, as well as many other goals which go far beyond the purely genetic

coding. In this respect, human systems are both more *open* and more *unpredictable* than non-human systems.

Problems of Complexity

We can summarize what we have discussed so far by saying that highly complex systems are: *self-stabilizing, goal-seeking, program following, self-reprogramming, anticipating, environment-modifying, self-replicating, self-maintaining and repairing, self-reorganizing,* and *self-programming.* These characteristics are listed approximately in order of increasing complexity, although a particular system may have one characteristic and lack another that precedes it. For instance, it would be much harder to build an automatic machine that is capable of reproducing itself than to build one that is capable of modifying its environment in a useful way, yet all living things do the harder task—reproduction—and many of them are unable to do the easier one. In general, however, the more complex a system is, the more likely it is to have most or all of the characteristics on this list.

Increasing complexity creates some advantages and some disadvantages. Compared with simpler systems, a highly complex system will normally be able to process more information, anticipate changes in the environment more accurately, learn more quickly, act more flexibly, and in general be able to respond more appropriately to a wider range of changing circumstances.

On the other hand, more complexity also means that the system has more subsystems to maintain and coordinate, there are more places for things to go wrong, and more energy and resources have to be spent on information gathering and processing. Every increase in complexity has a cost, and useless complications just decrease the efficiency of the whole system. In spite of this, most of the complexity in the systems around us is worthwhile, because it adds more stability and efficiency than it takes away. It nevertheless creates certain kinds of problems which we need to be aware of when we try to deal with these systems.

The Tragedy of the Commons: The first of these problems is that complex systems have to contain many subsystems and these subsystems may have goals which conflict with each other or are harmful to the bigger system. One of the best illustrations of this is a situation known as "the Tragedy of the Commons," after an essay of that name by ecologist Garrett Hardin.

Hardin used for the scene of his illustration the "commons," or *common pasture* of medieval England and colonial America. "Common" in this sense meant that all members of the community were entitled to graze their livestock there. The positive feedback loop involved in the use of the commons, from the point of view of the individual livestock owner, goes like this: "The more cows I have, the better off I will be. Feeding them is free, so I will increase the size of my herd as fast as I can."

But this creates a situation which each individual is powerless to avoid. As each person increases his herd, the number of cows grazing on the commons increases; after a certain point, there are enough cattle to eat the grass faster than it can grow back; when there is no more long grass left, the cows will then crop the remaining grass right down to the ground, killing the plants and leaving nothing but bare dirt. Soon the cows are all starving, and the entire village is faced with bankruptcy and possible starvation.

Notice that it does no good for any one villager to voluntarily keep the size of his herd down. If he refrains from putting more cows on the pasture, he simply leaves more grass for his neighbors' cattle, and increases the incentive for each of them to add still more. As a result, his unselfish action will *not* prevent the disaster, and he will be poorer in the meantime. Since each herdsman can see that it would be pointless to hold back, each one adds as many cows as he can until the inevitable disaster occurs.

The remarkable thing about this situation is that if *each* person makes the most sensible decision from his own point of view, the result is that *everyone* ends up much worse off. What is missing from the commons system is a negative feedback loop to limit the size of individual herds and, accordingly, the size of the total herd, to the level where it exactly matches the rate of growth of the grass.

There are several possible solutions. If there are 50 families in the village, for example, one solution would be to divide the commons into 50 lots and give one lot to each family. In that way, if a particular family put too many cows on their own lot and allowed the lot to become overgrazed, then that family would be the only one to suffer from it. This gives each family an incentive to keep its herd at the right level.

But putting up all those fences would be expensive, and cows are always knocking fences down or getting tangled up in them. It might be cheaper and simpler in the long run to give each family the right to graze a certain maximum number of cows in the open pasture. If the land can support 200 cows, each family would have the right to put a maximum of 4 cows on it.

Still another solution would be to hold an auction each year and auction off 200 grazing permits to whoever was willing to pay the most for them. The money could then be divided equally among the

members of the village. Whatever solution they choose, however, it will have to involve some kind of "government" regulation—what Hardin calls "mutual coercion, mutually agreed upon." The "tragedy" of the commons is that disaster is inevitable as long as the original rule of the commons is used. But the interesting thing is that if everyone agrees to give up some individual freedom to the larger system—the village as a whole—then everyone is better off as a result.

The commons problem is still with us in many ways. It typically occurs when the boundaries of a problem are bigger than the largest system which has the power to solve the problem. The original commons was a *village-wide* problem, but the power to make decisions about it was at the *individual* level. The solution was either to give the decision-making power to a system as big as the problem, such as a village council, or to divide the problem up into many small problems and give each of the individual decision makers exclusive responsibility for one piece of the problem.

But the second solution is not always possible. There is no way, for example, to fence off the atmosphere, so that pollution created in Newark remains solely Newark's problem, not Manhattan's problem as well. In these cases, the usual solution is to delegate authority upward to a higher-level system, such as the federal Environmental Protection Agency.

One advantage that the United States has, from a systems point of view, is that the area controlled by the national government is big enough to handle most

"The Yugoslavs can complain, but there is no way they can force the Italians to stop polluting."

problems which spill over more than one state. In areas like Europe, however, the countries are much smaller and "commons" problems are much more likely to spill over from one nation to another. When factories in Italy create pollution which harms people in Yugoslavia, there is no way to divide up the problem, and no really effective "higher level" to pass the problem up to. The Yugoslavs can complain, but there is really no way that they can force the Italians to stop polluting, unless they are willing to start a war.

Ultimately, as the world becomes more and more industrialized, problems like pollution become increasingly world-wide problems. Both the atmosphere and the ocean, where all pollutants end up, span the globe, so they really constitute a *global commons*. As the problems increase, we will eventually need an effective world government of some sort, with the power to make decisions on global problems at a global level. The United Nations is a step in this direction, but so far its member nations have not given it the power to control their behaivor.

The Cost of Information: Since the "tragedy of the commons" is caused by trying to cope with a problem at too low a level in a system, it would seem that it could be avoided by simply coping with all problems at the highest level of the system. However, this would mean that the top level of the system would have to make all of the decisions for every part of the system, which means that it would have to have all of the information necessary to make all of those decisions, and information is expensive to collect, store, and use.

Many people complain already about the size of the government bureaucracy, but just think how big it would have to be if every decision on every local matter—whether to hire a particular teacher, change part of a zoning code, fine a speeder, buy a new snowplow, repair a street—had to be made in Washington! People would have to spend hours and hours filling out forms and giving testimony on the simplest subjects, and then wait months or years for the forms to get to Washington, reach the right person to make the decision, and then be transmitted back again. Nothing would get done, the cost in time, money, and labor would be ridiculous, and the whole system would quickly grind to a halt.

In other words, we have a conflict here between two good rules of thumb. On the one hand, it is quicker, simpler, and cheaper to make decisions at the lowest level possible in the system. On the other hand, it is essential to make decisions at a high enough level in the system to avoid serious "commons" problems. The important thing to understand is that there is no perfect solution to this conflict. Shifting the control of a problem to a higher level may reduce conflicts between subsystems, but it also increases costs and reduces efficiency and flexibility. Giving control of a problem to the subsystems at a lower level increases speed and flexibility, but also increases the possibility for serious conflict.

"The government chooses to spend only enough money to make smuggling risky."

For most complex systems, the best rule of thumb seems to be: *"Make each decision at the lowest possible level, but be ready to shift the control of the situation to a higher level if a serious problem occurs."* Natural systems do this automatically. For example, you do not have to remember to breathe, or consciously think about which muscles to move when you are walking. As long as nothing goes wrong, you can let the lower levels of your nervous system deal with these tasks, and keep the highest level—your conscious mind—free for dealing with more important things. You only have to think about them when you choke, or get dizzy, or something else happens which the subsystems can't cope with.

With the economic and political systems, however, choosing the level at which to deal with a problem is not at all automatic. One the one hand, people often fail to recognize a serious "commons" problem when it occurs, and resent giving up their own freedom to do what they want without government interference; business's hostility to environmental regulations is an example. On the other hand, when people can see obvious imperfections in the system, they often are unaware of the high costs of removing those imperfections.

This brings us back to a point discussed in chapter three—the advantages of tolerating some sloppiness in a system. For example, smuggling is against the law, and it would be desirable to eliminate it completely. To do this, the government would have to know about every attempt to smuggle things into the country. To get this information, we would have to guard every inch of coastline and border and hire enough customs agents to completely search every person and thing entering the country. The cost of getting this information would obviously be much higher than solving the smuggling problem is worth, so the government chooses to spend only enough to make smuggling risky, even though that means allowing a good deal of smuggling to continue.

The property tax is another example. The tax on a piece of property is based on the property's value, but the problem is that property values are always changing. It is obviously unfair to you if the government thinks your house is worth twice as much as it really is, because then you'll have to pay twice as much tax as you should. Similarly, it is unfair to everybody else if the government values your building at only *half* of what it is worth, because then you won't have to pay your fair share. But to send trained and highly paid appraisers out at frequent intervals to examine every building in a community may be so costly that the system would be better off if it simply put up with some unfairness. If there is some way the people who are paying too much can appeal, they will have an incentive to do so and this will solve half the problem; it will then probably be cheaper to let the other group "get away with" paying too small a tax than it would be to spend the money to find out who they are and collect the additional tax.

It's easy to look at problems like smuggling and property taxes in this way, but most people have some issues which they get emotional about. If you feel very strongly that the government should do more about pornography, drug use, unemployment, abortion, racial discrimination, the sale of hand-guns, or some other issue, you may think it would be well worth the cost. Nevertheless, these are all problems which would be very difficult for the national government to *completely* solve—expensive not just in terms of money, but in terms of growth of government bureaucracy, loss of freedom and privacy, and disruption of other essential parts of the system. Unfortunately, any system has limited resources for collecting and processing information, and this means that it must make difficult and often unpleasant choices about which problems it should pay attention to and how hard it should try to solve them.

This does *not* mean, incidentally, that society should necessarily ignore the problems listed above. That is fundamentally a moral and political decision in

"Solving one problem almost always creates others"

each case. It does mean, however, that no society can be perfect—solving one problem almost always creates others—and people need to understand and have tolerance for some degree of sloppiness and unfairness in the system.

The Distortion of Feedback: Still another information problem is that complex systems depend on information to control the behavior of their subsystems, and this often creates an incentive for the subsystems to "lie" or at least to distort the information flow. For example, good academic grades and test scores are intended to be indicators of learning and achievement, but they are also the basis for admission to other schools and to good jobs. Since the students know about these potential rewards, a feedback loop is created which is supposed to look like this:

But if there are other ways to get good grades besides working harder and learning more, students will be tempted to take a short cut, such as studying only what will be on the exam, or cramming for the exam, or cheating, or trying to persuade the teacher to raise the grade, or falsifying the records of the grades. In other words, the student can try to manipulate the *symbol* (good grades) instead of changing the underlying reality (more learning) which the symbol is supposed to represent.

The same thing can happen to many other areas. If people are taxed on what they *say* their incomes are, they will be tempted to lie about how much money they make. If people in business and government are fired for making mistakes, they will be tempted to hide those mistakes from the people in charge instead of admitting mistakes and fixing them. If politicians need votes to get elected, they may be tempted to stuff the ballot box rather than persuade the voters. A company with a poor product will be tempted to lie to potential customers in its advertisements.

Grades, tax forms, work records, vote counts, and advertisements are all pieces of information which form essential parts of various feedback loops in the economic and political systems. If people think it is easier to manipulate the feedback loops by distorting the information than by changing what the information is supposed to represent, the quality of the information which the system gets will decrease and so will the efficiency of the system as a whole.

As a result, complex systems generally have to spend a great deal of effort and resources trying to prevent this distortion, either by "checking up" through other channels on the information it gets, or by making the information much harder to distort, or by making the penalties for cheating much higher than the rewards. This constant need to protect feedback loops from distortion simply adds to the cost of collecting information in the first place.

The Loss of Predictability: Finally, the flexibility that enables complex systems to survive in rapidly changing situations also results in a loss of predictability—that is, it reduces the availability of accurate information about what the system will do in the future. This is conspicuous in economic and political systems. A democracy, for example, is much more flexible than a rigid totalitarian society, but this flexibility also makes it harder to make effective long-range plans in a democracy. Similarly, a modern market economy is able to respond to changes more quickly and accurately than a controlled economy can. But this also makes it much more difficult to forecast economic conditions in a country like the U.S. than in, say, the People's Republic of China. Even comparing systems within the U.S., we can see where this holds true. For instance, it is easier for a civil service employee to predict what he will be doing five years from now than it is for a person working in a dynamic industry like electronics, where the products and manufacturing techniques change almost daily.

The result is that we pay a *price* for greater flexibility. We are more likely to waste time or money on job training that becomes useless, or investments that turn out not to be needed. Up to a point, an increase in flexibility increases the overall efficiency of the system so much that the price of uncertainty is worth paying. As the rate of change increases, however, the costs of uncertainty begin to climb more rapidly, and it becomes more and more important to keep them in mind and to minimize unnecessary changes and losses of predictability.

Summary:

At this point, you should begin to have a working familiarity with the basic ideas of systems thinking, including a feel for the common patterns of organization and behavior that characterize most dynamic systems. The next step is to apply some of these ideas to the big, complicated systems that make up the world we live in. In the second book of this series, we will look first at the ecological, economic, and political parts of our environment, and then at some of the problems affecting the total system.

Appendix: System Notes

In recent years, ecologists and system scientists have learned a great deal about how complex systems behave. In the process, they have discovered that many other apparently irrational folk customs have similarly valid bases. Some old rules of thumb have been updated and generalized in the writings of modern system thinkers, and some new insights about system behavior have been formulated. Together they make up a kind of modern "folk-wisdom" that can be helpful in coping with a complicated world.

What follows is a list of 28 of these system guidelines or rules of thumb gleaned from books, articles, speeches, and word-of-mouth. Many of them relate to or overlap one another, and have been grouped together accordingly. Sources, where identifiable, are given at the end.

These are rules of thumb, not absolute laws. The thinking behind each is sketched briefly, and you may find some more convincing than others. That's not really important, however, as long as they are provocative and help you make sense of some kinds of system behavior that don't seem, at first glance, to make any sense at all.

System Notes

1. *Everything is connected to everything else.* Real life is lived in a complex world system where all the subsystems overlap and affect each other. The common mistake is to deal with one subsystem in isolation, as if it didn't connect with anything else. This almost always backfires as other subsystems respond in unanticipated ways.

2. *You can never do just one thing.* This follows from rule #1: in addition to the immediate effects of an action, there will always be other consequences of it which ripple through the system.

3. *There is no "away."* Another corollary of #1. In natural ecosystems, in particular, you can move something from one place to another, you can transform it into something else, but you can't get rid of it. As long as it is on the Earth, it is part of the global ecosystem. The industrial poisons, pollutants, insecticides, and radioactive materials that we've tried to "throw away" in the past have all too often come back to haunt us because people didn't understand this rule.

4. *TANSTAAFL: There Ain't No Such Thing As A Free Lunch.* Years ago, bars used to offer a "free lunch" as a way to draw customers. Of course, the drinks in those bars cost twice as much, so the lunches weren't really "free" at all. Similarly, in complex systems, what looks like the cheapest solution to a problem often turns out to be the most expensive one in the long run. TANSTAAFL is a way of saying, "Don't expect something for nothing, there's always a hidden cost somewhere."

5. *Nature knows best.* Natural ecosystems have evolved over millions of years, and everything in them has a role to play. Be very suspicious of any proposal to alter or eliminate an apparently "useless" part of the system. If it looks useless, that just means that you don't understand its function, and the risk of doing harm is that much greater. (For example, people have been draining "useless" marshes and swamps for centuries. Now, it turns out that these areas are vital for removing water pollution and as breeding grounds for economically important wildlife and fisheries. An area worth $10,000 as dry land may produce $100,000 worth of fish a year as a marsh.) When in doubt, be careful, and always try to find a "natural" solution to a problem if at all possible.

6. *It ain't what you don't know that hurts you; it's what you DO know that ain't so.* Beware of false assumptions about system behavior. When we are *sure* of something, we usually don't bother to look for proof that it is true and we may be blind to evidence that it is false. We are much more likely to make really big blunders when we act on false assumptions than when we are uncertain and aware of our own uncertainty.

7. *"Obvious solutions" do more harm than good.* All complex systems use negative feedback to *negate* external changes in the system. If you try to change something in the direct, "obvious" way, the system is going to treat your efforts like any other outside influence and do its best to neutralize them. The more energy you waste fighting the system head on, the more energy it will waste fighting back, and any gains you make will be only temporary at best. Finally, if you try hard enough and long enough, you will exhaust the system's ability to fight back—at which point the system will break down completely!

8. *Look for high leverage points.* Nearly every feedback system has weak spots. These are almost always the control points which measure the system's behavior and determine its response to change. The best way to change a system's behavior is either to change the "setting" of the control unit or to change the information which the control unit receives. If you want to make a cold house warmer, turn the thermostat up or stick an ice pack on it, but don't build a fire in the fireplace—it won't do any good.

9. *Nothing grows forever.* The exponential growth curves produced by positive feedback keep on growing only in mathematics. In the real world, growth *always* stops sooner or later, and the faster the growth, the sooner it will stop. If the Earth's

human population could continue to grow at its current rate for another 7 centuries, we would be the only living things on the planet. After just ten more centuries, the mass of bodies would outweigh the entire rest of the planet—an obvious impossibility. If energy use continued to grow at its current rate for another 400 years, the surface of the earth would be hotter than the sun. And at current rates of growth in food consumption, we would have to eat every thing on the planet in a single year only 5 centuries from now. Obviously, these projections are ridiculous and the growth of population, energy use, and food consumption will stop long before such extremes are reached. The question is, how soon and in what way?

10. *Don't fight positive feedback; support negative feedback instead.* Don't poison pests, support their predators. Don't order people to have fewer children, make it more profitable for them to have small families instead. Don't ration energy, raise the price instead (and give the money back by cutting taxes somewhere else, like the social security tax). And so on. England used a version of this rule for centuries in European politics. Whenever one nation or group got too strong, England would throw its support to the weaker side. (Don't try to weaken your enemy, strengthen your enemy's enemies instead.)

11. *Don't try to control the players, just change the rules.* When the National Football League wanted to make football games a bit more exciting, it could have ordered quarterbacks to throw more passes. If it had, teams would have looked for ways to evade the order, perhaps by throwing a few more short, safe passes, and the game would still have been dull. Instead, the league changed the rules slightly so that pass plays would have a better chance of working. As a result, teams were aggressive about taking advantage of the new opportunities to pass. The same principle applies in economics, politics, science, education, and many other areas. If the system tries to make choices *for* people, the people will try to outwit the system. It is much more effective to change the "rules of the game" so that it is to most people's *advantage* to make the choices that are good for the whole system.

12. *Don't make rules that can't be enforced.* If many people want to disobey a law and nearly all of them are able to get away with it, then the law will not be obeyed. But this gets people used to disobeying laws, and it reduces respect for laws in general. It also creates ideal opportunities for corruption, blackmail, and the acceptance of organized crime. A society that really gets serious about enforcing unenforceable laws can tear itself apart. (See, for example, the tremendous damage done by witch-hunts, inquisitions, and civil wars that result from enforcing laws against thinking certain kinds of religious or political thoughts.) The same problem

arises in business, government, and many other kinds of systems, where a higher level system is weakened by trying to *overcontrol* lower sub-systems.

13. *There are no simple solutions.* Real-life systems are big, messy, complicated things, with problems to match. Genuine solutions require careful thought for their effect on the whole system. Anyone who tries to sell you a simple answer—"All we have to do is . . . and everything will be perfect!"—is either honestly dumb, or dishonest and probably running for office.

14. *Good intentions are not enough.* Few things are more painful than trying to do good and finding out that you've done a great deal of harm instead. Simple compassion and simple morality are inadequate in a complex world. The bumbling missionary causes tragedy because he follows his heart without using his head to try to understand the whole situation.

15. *High morality depends on accurate prophecy.* You cannot judge the morality of an action unless you have some idea of what the consequences of the action will be. According to this point of view, an action cannot be good if it has evil results, and everyone has a moral obligation to *try* to foresee, as well as possible, what the results of various decisions will be.

16. *If you can't make people self-sufficient, your aid does more harm than good.* This usually comes up in discussing problems of poverty or hunger, where temporary relief often postpones the disaster at the cost of making it much worse when it comes. It is not really an argument against helping, but an argument against half-way measures. Ghandi said the same thing in a more positive way: "If you give me a fish, I eat for a day; if you teach me to fish, I eat for a lifetime."

17. *There are no final answers.* As Ken Boulding put it, "If all environments were stable, the well-adapted would simply take over the earth and the evolutionary process would stop. In a period of environmental change, however, *it is the adaptable, not the well-adapted who survive.*" This applies to social systems as well as natural ones. In a time of rapid change, like the present, the best "solution" to a problem is often one that just keeps the problem under control while keeping as many options open for the future as possible.

18. *Every solution creates new problems.* The auto solved the horse-manure pollution problem and created an air pollution problem. Modern medicine brought us longer, healthier lives—and a population explosion that threatens to produce a global famine. Television brings us instant access to vital information and world events—and a mind-numbing barrage of banality and violence. And so on. The important thing is to try to *anticipate* the new problems and decide whether we prefer them to

the problems we are currently trying to solve. Sometimes the "best" solution to one problem just creates a worse problem. There may even be *no* solution to the new problem. On the other hand, an apparently "inferior" solution to the original problem may be much better for the whole system in the long run.

19. *Loose systems are often better.* Diverse, decentralized systems often seem disorganized and wasteful, but they are almost always more stable, flexible, and efficient in the long run than "neater" systems. In Boulding's terms (#17), highly adaptable systems look sloppy compared to systems that are well-adapted to a specific situation, but the sloppy-looking systems are the ones that will survive. In addition, systems which are loose enough to tolerate moderate fluctuations in things like population levels, food supply, or prices, are more efficient than systems which waste energy and resources on tighter controls.

20. *Don't be fooled by system cycles.* All negative feedback loops create oscillations—some large, some small. For some reason, many people are unable to deal with or believe in cyclical patterns, especially if the cycles are more than two or three years in length. If the economy has been growing steadily for the last four years, nearly everyone will be optimistic. They simply project their recent experience ahead into the future, forgetting that a recession becomes more likely the longer the boom continues. Similarly, everyone is gloomiest at the bottom of a recession, just when rapid growth is most likely.

Highly visible job categories often fluctuate in the same way. When a temporary oversupply of workers develops in a particular field, everyone talks about the big surplus and young people are steered away from the field. Within a few years, this creates a shortage, jobs go begging, and young people are frantically urged into the field—which creates a surplus. Obviously, the best time to start training for such a job is when people have been talking about a surplus for several years and few others are entering it. That way, you finish your training just as the shortage develops.

The problem is that most people have short memories and tend to project the recent past forward on a straight line. As a result you get this kind of pattern:

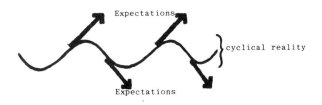

21. *Remember the Golden Mean.* When people face a serious problem, they tend to overvalue anything that helps solve it. They mobilize their energies and fight hard to solve the problem, and often keep right on going after the problem is solved and the solution is becoming a new problem. When most children died before their tenth birthdays, a high birth rate was essential for survival and societies developed powerful ways to encourage people to have large families. When the death rate is reduced, a high birth rate becomes a liability, but all those strong cultural forces keep right on encouraging large families, and it can take generations for people's attitudes to change. Like the man who eats himself to death as an adult because he was always hungry as a child, people tend to forget that too much of something can be as bad as too little. They assume that if more of something is good, a lot more must be better—but it often isn't. The trick is to recognize these situations and try to swing the pendulum back to the middle whenever it swings toward *either* extreme.

22. *Beware the empty compromise.* There are also times when the middle ground is worse than either extreme. There's an old, old fable about an ass who starved to death halfway between two bales of hay because it couldn't make up its mind which one to eat first. Sometimes you just have to choose, because a compromise won't work. The only way to tell is to examine the entire system carefully and try to anticipate what the results of different decisions will be.

23. *Don't be a boiled frog.* Some systems are designed so that they can react to any change that is larger than a certain amount, but they can't respond to changes that are below that threshold. For example, if a frog is put in a pan of hot water, he will jump right out. But if he is put in a pan of cool water and the water is then gradually heated up, the frog will happily sit there and let himself be cooked. As long as the change is slow enough, it doesn't trigger a response. Sometimes a country can use this tactic to defeat an enemy in a patient series of small steps. Each step weakens the opponent a little bit, but is "not worth going to war over," until finally the victim is too weak to resist an attack. (These are sometimes called "salami-slicing tactics." "Divide and conquer" is another version of the same thing.) While a healthy system shouldn't overreact to small changes, it has to be able to identify and respond to a *series* of small changes that will bring disaster if allowed to continue.

24. *Watch out for thresholds.* Most systems change pretty gradually. But some systems are designed to switch abruptly from one kind of behavior to a completely different kind. Sometimes this is a defense against the "boiled frog" problem. ("He's meek as a lamb until you push him too far. Then you'd better watch out!") In other cases, it's a way

of avoiding "empty compromises" (#22). But most often it's because the system, or a subsystem of it, has exhausted its reserves for coping with some pressure on it. (See the discussion of exposure and heat-stroke in Part One.) This can be disastrous if you are relying on a system that has seemed able to absorb a lot of abuse and it suddenly collapses as a result of something apparently trivial. Democracies, market economies, and natural ecosystems are all prone to behave in this way. They seem so sturdy that we can kick them around, interfere with subsystem after subsystem, increase the load more and more, and they will always bounce back. But we can never be sure which straw is going to break the camel's back.

25. *Competition is often cooperation in disguise.* A chess player may push himself to the limit in his desire to defeat his opponent, and yet be very upset if he finds out that his opponent let him win. What appears to be a fierce competition on one level is actually part of a larger system in which both players *cooperate* in a ritual that gives both of them pleasure. Not "doing your best" is a violation of that cooperative agreement. Similarly, the competitions between two lawyers in a courtroom is an essential part of a larger process in which lawyers, judge, and jury *cooperate* in a search for just answers. Businesses cooperate to keep the economy running efficiently by competing with each other in the marketplace. Political parties cooperate in running a democracy by competing with each other at the polls. And so on.

How do you tell cooperative competition from destructive competition? In cooperative competition, the opponents are willing to fight by the rules and accept the outcome of a fair contest, even if it goes against them, because they know the game will continue and they will get another chance. One reason extremist movements like communism or fascism are dangerous in a democracy is that they turn politics into destructive competition, aimed at a *total* victory which would put an end to the competition.

26. *Bad boundaries make bad governments.* Unlike most cities, St. Louis is not part of a larger county. St. Louis County surrounds the city and keeps it from expanding its city limits. As a result, the communities in the county have become parasites on the city, using the city's commercial and cultural resources but contributing nothing toward the cost of maintaining them. As long as there is a boundary that splits the metropolitan area in half, and no government with authority over the whole area, the county will keep getting richer and the city will keep getting poorer until urban decay completely destroys it. Similar boundary problems afflict states, nations, ecosystems, and economic regions. As a general rule, the system with responsibility for a problem should include the entire problem area; authority must be congruent with responsibility, or a commons problem (#27) results.

27. *Beware the Tragedy of the Commons.* A "commons" problem occurs when subsystems in a competitive relationship with each other are forced to act in ways that are destructive of the whole system. Usually, the source of the problem is the right of a subsystem to receive the whole benefit from using a resource while paying only a small part of the cost for it. The solution is either to divide the common resource up (not always possible) or to limit access to it.

28. *Foresight always wins in the long run.* Solutions to problems affecting complex systems usually take time. If we wait until the problem develops and then react to it, there may not be time for any good solutions before a crisis point is reached. If we look ahead and *anticipate* a problem, however, we usually have more choices and a better chance of heading the problem off before it disrupts things. Reacting to problems means letting the system control us. Only by using foresight do we have a real chance to control the system. Or: Those who do not try to create the future they want must endure the future they get.

Sources

Although some of these guidelines are associated with particular people, it is impossible to trace most of the concepts back to specific originators with any confidence. Rule #1 was a favorite precept of anothropologist Franz Boaz. Rules 2, 14, 16, and 27 are associated with Garrett Hardin. Rules 3 and 5 were either coined or popularized by Barry Commoner. #4 is associated with Commoner and science fiction author Robert Heinlein, among others. #6 is an old idea, but the words apparently come from humorist Josh Billings. #7 is associated with Jay Forrester. #9 is also an old idea; it has been emphasized by Isaac Asimov, Paul Ehrlich, Hardin, Forrester, and Donella Meadows, among others. #15 is a quote from John Platt's book, *The Step to Man.* The Boulding quote in #17 is from *The Meaning of the 20th Century.* Most of the rest are "in general use"—i.e., not especially associated with an originator or a popularizer. They have generally been paraphrased or re-stated for this book.